513·85

MATHEMATICAL
MODELS

MATHEMATICAL MODELS

BY

H. MARTYN CUNDY

PROFESSOR OF MATHEMATICS
UNIVERSITY OF MALAWI

AND

A. P. ROLLETT

SECOND EDITION

OXFORD
AT THE CLARENDON PRESS

Oxford University Press, Ely House, London W. 1

GLASGOW NEW YORK TORONTO MELBOURNE WELLINGTON
CAPE TOWN IBADAN NAIROBI DAR ES SALAAM LUSAKA ADDIS ABABA
DELHI BOMBAY CALCUTTA MADRAS KARACHI LAHORE DACCA
KUALA LUMPUR SINGAPORE HONG KONG TOKYO

First published 1951
Reprinted from corrected sheets of the first edition
1954, 1956, 1957
Second edition 1961
Reprinted 1962, 1964, 1966, 1968, 1971, 1972

Printed in Great Britain
at the University Press, Oxford
by Vivian Ridler
Printer to the University

PREFACE TO THE SECOND EDITION

SINCE this book was first published nine years ago it has brought to the authors a steady flow of correspondence from most parts of the English-speaking world. It has been most gratifying to know of so many to whom the book has given pleasure. It has been most helpful to receive criticisms, and suggestions for improvement, which have sprung from practical experience in universities and in every type of school, and which have come from both staff and pupils. Many of these suggestions have been incorporated in this new edition. Three correspondents in particular should be gratefully mentioned: Mr. Dorman Luke, of West Palm Beach, Florida, Mr. A. R. Pargeter of Southampton, and Mr. R. F. Wheeler of Hull, to whom much new material is due.

Little of the old edition has disappeared—chiefly what was proved to be less practicable. The major addition is Chapter VI, on Logic and Computing, which it is hoped will be found useful as an introduction to a fascinating field of considerable topical interest and importance. Part of this, and certain other material, has already appeared in *The Mathematical Gazette*, to the Editor of which our thanks are due for ready permission to reprint.

A special word of thanks must be reserved for Mr. R. W. Ford, who prepared all the drawings for this book; his ready co-operation and skilful draughtsmanship reveal the patience of the true craftsman and their monument is to be seen on almost every page. Words of ours would be superfluous to commend the care and skill of the staff of the Clarendon Press; for their courtesy and encouragement we would subscribe our warmest thanks.

H. M. C.
A. P. R.

1960

PREFACE TO THE FIRST EDITION

'I HAVE often been surprised that Mathematics, the quint-
essence of Truth, should have found admirers so few and so
languid. Frequent consideration and minute scrutiny have at
length unravelled the cause; viz. that though Reason is feasted,
Imagination is starved; whilst Reason is luxuriating in its
proper Paradise, Imagination is wearily travelling on a dreary
desert. To assist Reason by the stimulus of Imagination is the
design of the following production.'

So wrote S. T. Coleridge to his brother in 1791, when he himself was a boy of 17 at Christ's Hospital. The 'production' to
which he refers was a problem of Euclid, expressed in verse. If
the words are in any sense an apt introduction to this present
work, it is a different kind of imagination to which it must lay
claim, and, one may add, a more essentially mathematical kind.

This book was born in the classroom, and arose from the
spontaneous interest of a Mathematical Sixth in the construction of simple models. A desire to show that even in mathematics one could have fun led to an exhibition of the results and
attracted considerable attention throughout the school. Since
then the Sherborne collection has grown, ideas have come from
many sources, and widespread interest has been shown. It
seems therefore desirable to give permanent form to the lessons
of experience so that others can benefit by them and be encouraged to undertake similar work.

A word may be added here about the functions of the respec-
tive authors. Between them their experience extends from 1927
to the present time, and they have made or supervised the
making of practically every model mentioned in this book.
The second author provided the initial stimulus for much of
the work and also a constant flow of ideas and inspiration.
The actual writing has of necessity devolved mainly upon the
first author, and he is responsible for the presentation of the
material. But the book is in a real sense a joint effort, though
not perhaps a collaboration of the orthodox type.

The authors are indebted to Mr. B. J. Banner for his photographs of the regular and Archimedean polyhedra: to Messrs. Newton and Co. for diagrams of curves drawn with the twin-elliptic pendulum: to Professor H. S. M. Coxeter for some of the drawings and for his friendly interest and encouragement: to Mr. F. G. Mee for reading the proofs: and finally to the staff of the Clarendon Press for all the help and advice that they have given. The provenance of ideas can never be fully acknowledged, but the reader who is familiar with the books listed in the Bibliography will recognize all too readily the origin of much that is contained in the following pages. There is here very little originality of concept, but only that originality which inheres in anything that is individually made. And this the authors hope will be as much the reader's as their own.

H. M. C.
A. P. R.

Sherborne, 1951

CONTENTS

LIST OF PLATES

between pages 136–7

I

THE USE AND CONSTRUCTION OF MODELS

MATHEMATICS is often regarded as the bread and butter of science. If the butter is omitted, the result is indigestion, loss of appetite, or both. The purpose of this book is to suggest some ways of buttering the bread. The human mind can seldom accept completely abstract ideas; they must be derived from, or illustrated by, concrete examples. Here the reader will find ways of providing for himself tangible objects which will bring that necessary contact with reality into the symbolic world of mathematics.

1.1. WHAT IS A MODEL?

In theory, any figure drawn on paper is a tangible aid to the understanding, and there would be some justification in including this in the title, for the earliest use of the word 'model' denoted a set of architect's plans. We shall, however, include here only such figures as possess intrinsic interest and are outside the ordinary run of figures which are easily available elsewhere. We are more concerned with solid objects, 'figures' in solid geometry, moving diagrams, and mechanisms. The plane models we shall describe are for the most part made *of* paper or card, as distinct from figures made of ink *on* paper. There is, however, a section (2.4) on curves and loci, included for their peculiar interest. The models relate mainly to 'elementary' mathematics, though there are some that stand outside the ordinary work in a school. The reader is well advised to see the collections of models in places like the Science Museum, or some university mathematical departments, but our aim here is rather less ambitious.†

† There is a beautiful collection of polyhedral models in wire and cardboard at Winchester College. These were made by three boys, F. J. Dyson, M. S. and H. C. Longuet–Higgins, two of whom have later become university professors.

1.2. The Use of Models

The main use of a model is the pleasure derived from making it. When it is made it can be used to demonstrate the fact which it illustrates. Finally, it may form part of a permanent collection of similar constructions. People have collected many stranger things than polyhedra on occasion. If words must be found, we can describe these uses as the creative, demonstrative, and collective uses of models.

The creative value of a model is there for anybody who will take the trouble to make it. A mathematician who cannot express himself in other ways may be able to make an attractive model, and to make it well. In many cases great technical skill is not required, and some of the most complicated models described in the following pages require nothing beyond care and patience. Further, the materials are not usually expensive, and even scrap can often be used. The keen model-maker is always on the look-out for possible raw material.

The demonstrative use of the model will appeal more to the professional teacher of mathematics. There is no doubt that we all appreciate and remember much more easily the properties of something we have actually seen; even more so if we have actually made it.

Some models in this book are suitable for 'mass production' by a class; others are more suitable for demonstration. The wise teacher will know best how to use any particular idea which he finds here and we have not felt it our duty to tell him. We only hope that plenty of ideas will be found.

The collective value of models is associated with a personal collection, or a mathematical exhibition. To set out to make for oneself a full set of regular and Archimedean polyhedra, or examples of all the quadric surfaces, or even a complete set of sketches of the various types of cubic curve, is a hobby which satisfies one's acquisitive instinct, demands patience, teaches skill, and can bring much pleasure. A good mathematical exhibition always arouses interest. It is an opportunity for many to participate; it stimulates enthusiasm and an awareness of the aesthetic value of mathematics, as well as its pervasiveness. It is a mistake to suppose that what is not fully understood is dull or will not attract attention: many enjoy a fugue without understanding the technicalities of its structure.

1.3. MATERIALS FOR MODELS

Suitable material for each model described in the following pages is usually suggested with the description. In general no elaborate materials are required. Except of course for exhibition purposes, crudeness of construction is no drawback to the usefulness of a model, and may even be an advantage in stimulating someone else to do better! The best models are those which are made from things which are ready to hand. The following suggestions may be useful.

1.3.1. Material suitable for flat sheets can be obtained from backs of old exercise books, manilla filing folders, cartridge paper, plain postcards, or pasteboard in various thicknesses. An obliging printer may be able to supply offcuts. More durable sheets can be made of sheet metal, cut from old tins and cans, hardboard, or plywood. Thick plasterboard is useful for building up a layered surface: i.e. a relief map from contours. Glass, celluloid, and 'Perspex' have the advantage of transparency; polythene sheeting can now be bought fairly cheaply.

Disks can be made from toy wheels, plastic saucers, and the like. Broken plastic beakers can have their bases cut off with a hacksaw and polished up with glasspaper. Cork mats have their uses—they do not slip so easily as plastics.

Straight lines can be embodied in a variety of ways: embroidery thread (*coton à broder*), coloured twine, plastic (polyvinyl) thread, 'Shirlastic', nylon fish-line, round elastic, and gut; rigid lines can be made of knitting needles, drinking straws (for temporary display!), 'Meccano' or 'Bayko' rods, cocktail-sticks or skewers; curved lines from piano wire or plastic-covered electrical wire.

'Meccano' is an obvious source of straight and curved strip; thick card, metal strip, steel strapping from crates, dowel-rod, miniature railway rail, curtain rail (flat or ⊥-section), all come in useful. Circular rings are everywhere, from the steel washer to the hula-hoop. To join flat links, use paper-fasteners, eyelets, or gut rivets, made by heating the ends of short lengths of violin string. Drawing-pins, especially those with coloured heads, are always handy.

1.3.2. Adhesives are legion. Quick-drying cements like Balsa cement or *clear* 'Bostik' are most useful; so are impact adhesives such as 'Evostik' or the epoxy resins such as 'Araldite'. 'Durofix' is best for celluloid, or use a solvent such as amyl acetate; for 'Perspex', use ethylene dichloride, or the cement supplied by the manufacturers. Nail-polish remover (acetone) can also be used for some plastics. Glass is awkward to cement, though Canada balsam or glass cement can be used.

1.3.3. Tools, etc.

Razor blades and steel rule	File
Coping-saw	Plane
Fine tenon-saw	Hammer
Hack-saw	Screwdriver
Wheelbrace and drills	Shears and scissors
Compasses	Wire-cutters
Eyelet punch	Glass-cutter
Soldering iron and cored	Glass-paper and emery cloth
solder	Household scouring powder
Small cramp	Metal polish

1.3.4. Pegboard. This is a most useful material for graphical displays of all kinds. To make the most of it, a sheet should be permanently mounted in a frame, and painted with lines at intervals of 5 and 10 holes like ordinary squared paper. Pegs with solid heads can be obtained in various shapes and colours. Some should have their heads drilled to take wire or elastic; if a few have two holes drilled at right angles they will serve for double-points of curves. Points can be 'plotted' with pegs with great rapidity. The only restriction is, of course, that coordinates must be an integral number of units. If piano wire is then threaded through the drill-holes a surprisingly accurate curve is obtained with no trouble at all. Elastic (round) serves for straight lines. Letters and figures which can be pegged directly into the board can be obtained from firms of shopfitters. The possibilities of a little quite simple equipment for striking displays are endless.

1.3.5. Miscellaneous. Most models look better if well painted. Metal strips are best painted with quick-drying dopes; cardboard with enamels (high-gloss paints); flat diagrams with poster-paints. Use good brushes, and keep separate those used for the various kinds of paint. Gummed sheets of coloured paper can be bought and are sometimes useful. Plastics are self-coloured, and different coloured threads, sheets, and wire should be obtained if required

The Meccano and Trix systems are flexible and therefore useful. A good thread-cutting die for metal rod or knitting-needles, etc., is a sound investment, but be sure that you can get nuts easily to match the thread. Balsa wood, beloved of the model aircraft enthusiast, has limited applicability in this field. Its extreme lightness is not needed, and the ease with which it is broken or deformed is a grave disadvantage. But the balsa wood cement is very useful since it dries rapidly.

It is not, of course, suggested that all these things are necessary, or that the model-maker should begin by laying in a stock of them all. The best way is to get started and buy things only as you need them. Many of these things need not be bought at all, since models can often be made from scrap or pieces which are too small for any other purpose. On the other hand, good tools are worth having, and will long outlast cheap or 'toy' substitutes.

The appearance of a model depends to a great extent on small details. For exhibition purposes where the best results are desired, accurate work is essential, and careful attention must be given to 'finish'. Good, even painting needs care and practice. Polishing requires patience. It is worth mentioning that all household cleansing-powders, in spite of the advertisements which boost their non-scratch properties, are excellent mild abrasives, used slightly damp, and will grind glass finely if rubbed between two panes. They are also useful for rubbing out scratches from metal or 'Perspex', leaving a fine matt surface which can be worked smooth if desired with metal polish. The human palm is the best polishing base!

A collection of models will need labelling. Advice can be sought from an artist or from books on the subject of lettering, but again practice and clean straight strokes are the best recipe for attractive results.

II

MODELS IN PLANE GEOMETRY

2.1. Dissections

The fascination of dissection is universal. To substantiate this statement we have only to call to mind the popularity of the jig-saw puzzle, the frequency with which dissection puzzles still

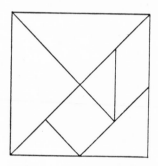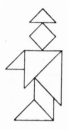

Fig. 1

appear in illustrated papers, and the continued sale for mosaics and similar toys. As a diversion we give diagrams of two of these. The first is the famous Chinese traditional pastime known as tangrams which used to be, and perhaps still is, marketed by a firm of toy manufacturers in this country. The square shown in the diagram (Fig. 1) is dissected into seven pieces: a small square whose side we take as the unit; five isosceles right-angled triangles, one with hypotenuse 2 units, two with unit equal sides, and two with equal sides of 2 units; and a parallelogram with unit base and unit height, the angle between two of its sides being 45°. From these pieces a large number of figures can be made, two of which are given as examples. A more ambitious design is shown in Fig. 2; in this case an egg is dissected and rearranged to form the outline of various birds; again a variety of other objects can be produced with a little ingenuity. A puzzle of this type was on the market several years ago; the outlines only of various figures were given, the object being to construct them from the pieces. It has been claimed that a feeling for congruence and incommensurable lengths can be obtained by such means. These designs can be cut very easily from thin plastic if a permanent set of pieces is required.

2.1.1. Area dissections. These dissections are used to show the equivalence of figures in the theory of area. They can be cut from paper or thin card. In most cases the construction of the figures is simple enough for beginners in the study of area to perform the dissections for themselves. Fig. 3 shows a method of demonstrating the equivalence of parallelograms on the same base and between the same parallels. A rectangle $ABCD$ is first cut from card, or a postcard may be used. A straight cut removes the triangle AXD, which can be laid down so that AD falls along BC; in this way the parallelogram $PQRS$ is built up. Different cuts from equal postcards will lead to different parallelograms, but all have equal bases and heights. The formal proof follows at once.

2.1.2. Area of a triangle. The fact that the area of a triangle is half that of a parallelogram on the same base with the same height follows immediately from the fact that two congruent triangles can actually be fitted together to form the parallelogram.

There is, however, a direct way of dissecting a triangle to form a rectangle. Fig. 4 makes the construction clear: X, Y are the mid-points of AB, AC, and AN is perpendicular to XY. It is of course necessary for the angles at B and C to be acute. The important fact also emerges from this dissection that XY is parallel to BC. Further, by moving the triangle LXB so that LB lies along MC, the method of proof is indicated.

A neat way of showing this same dissection is by folding. Cut the triangle ABC out of paper (Fig. 5) and fold along XY, XP, YQ. The resulting figure is a doubled rectangle $XYPQ$. Incidentally, another important fact emerges, namely, that the sum of the angles A, B, and C is $180°$, since these three angles exactly fit together, after the folding, at D.

Fig. 2

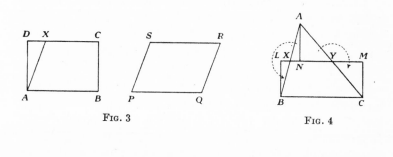

Fig. 3

Fig. 4

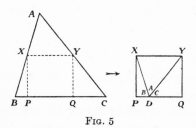

Fig. 5

2.1.3. Area of a trapezium. Three dissections are shown in the diagrams which demonstrate the formula for the area in each of the three forms $\frac{1}{2}\{h(a+b)\}$, $h \times \frac{1}{2}(a+b)$, $\frac{1}{2}h \times (a+b)$. In Fig. 6 two congruent trapezia are used, together making the

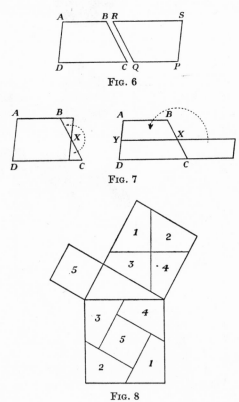

FIG. 6

FIG. 7

FIG. 8

parallelogram of area $h(a+b)$. In Fig. 7 only the one trapezium is used; the points X and Y are mid-points. In each case the trapezium is cut into two parts which are rearranged to form a parallelogram; in the first case the height is h and the base $\frac{1}{2}(a+b)$; in the second the height is $\frac{1}{2}h$ and the base $(a+b)$.

2.1.4. Theorem of Pythagoras. There are many proofs of this famous theorem which involve dissection; the best known is probably Perigal's, shown in Fig. 8. This is, however, a difficult dissection to carry out and its correctness is not easy to demonstrate formally. A simpler demonstration is shown in Fig. 9 which gives the equivalent squares as the difference between a fixed square and four movable triangles. To make a model, four set squares can be used for the triangles and a

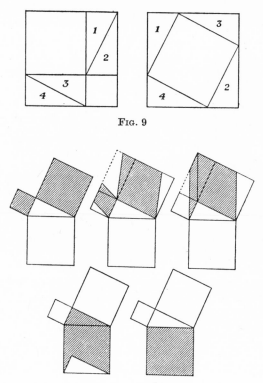

FIG. 9

FIG. 10

hollow square frame of the correct dimensions cut to accommodate them.

Neither of these dissections is connected with the Euclidean proof, which proceeds on quite different lines. Fig. 10 shows in visual form the equivalence of areas involved in this proof, but an actual dissection based on it would have eight pieces, whereas the two preceding figures involve only five.

2.1.5. General dissection. It can be shown that if two rectilinear figures are equivalent, each can be dissected into a finite number of pieces which can be rearranged to form the other.† This is in general a complicated procedure, but some particular cases are attractively simple, one of which is shown in Fig. 11. Here an equilateral triangle is dissected into four pieces only which can be rearranged to form the equivalent square.

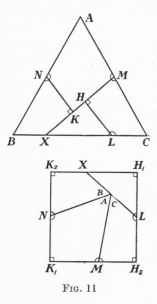

First find the side of the square by the usual construction as the mean proportional between half the base and the height of the triangle. Let M, N be the mid-points of AC and AB. Cut off MX, with X on BC, equal to the side of the equivalent square. Cut off $XL = \frac{1}{2}BC$, and drop the perpendiculars LH, NK from L, N to MX. If the four resulting pieces are hinged at L, M, N and rotated, they can be closed up into the square $K_1 K_2 H_1 H_2$ as in the second diagram. The formal proof is left to the reader, and shows incidentally that $KX = HM$. A model can be made of metal plates; accurate work will be needed in making the hinges.

Fig. 11

Further examples of dissection of this general type can be found in Kraitchik, *Mathematical Recreations*, pp. 193–8.

2.1.6. Puzzle dissections. H. E. Dudeney was a master-hand at producing puzzles of this type. His dissected-T puzzle is on the market today, in red plastic. Other well-known puzzles of his are: to cut a Greek cross into 4 or 5 pieces which can be rearranged to form a square; to cut two Greek crosses into 4 or 5 pieces which can be rearranged to form a square; to cut a square into 5 pieces which can be rearranged to form an octagon. Solutions are shown in Figs. 12 and 13.

This last example is interesting because it depends on a general

† A. Mineur, *Mathesis* (1931), pp. 150–2; Rouse Ball, *Mathematical Recreations and Essays*, revised by Coxeter, pp. 89–91.

idea. If two regular patterns—in this case one of squares and octagons (4.8² Fig. 57) and another of two different sizes of square—with the same area of unit cell are superposed, a dissection of the unit cell of one into the unit cell of the other can

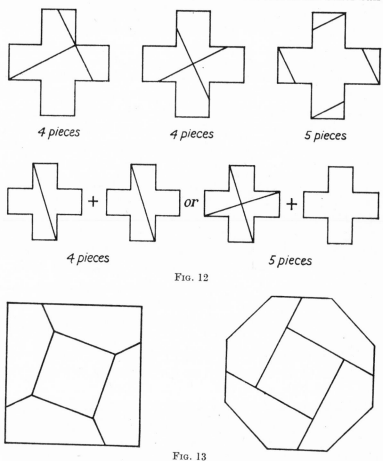

4 pieces   4 pieces   5 pieces

4 pieces   5 pieces

Fig. 12

Fig. 13

be obtained. The patterns are best drawn on tracing paper and suitable positions can be found by trial. The Greek cross dissections can also be obtained in this way, by superposing a pattern of squares of side √5 on one of unit squares.

2.1.7. Similar figures. An interesting dissection is shown in Fig. 14 in which a dodecagon is cut into twelve congruent pieces, which can be added to an equal dodecagon to make a similar figure with an edge √2 times as great. Each piece is an equilateral triangle plus half a square; six of the pieces must be turned over.

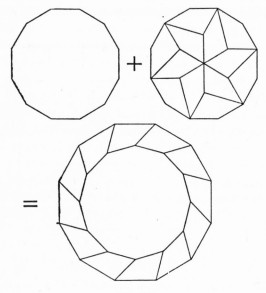

Fig. 14

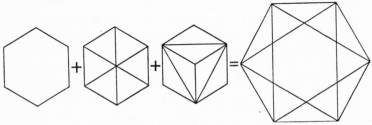

Fig. 15

The same thing can be done with three hexagons: two are cut up, each into six congruent pieces, but different in the two cases (Fig. 15). The original hexagon together with these twelve pieces can be reassembled to form a hexagon of side √3 times that of the original ones.

Dissections of an area into four areas, congruent to one

another and similar to the original, but with half its linear dimensions, are numerous.†

These provide elegant verifications of the law which states that the areas of similar figures are in the ratio of the squares of corresponding linear dimensions.

2.1.8. Pentominoes. This is the name given in America to a puzzle which has recently been on sale in this country. It consists of a set of 12 plastic pieces, which represent all the ways of arranging five squares in a single unit. The puzzle as supplied is in a box in the form of a 10×6 rectangle; the pieces can be fitted into this in 2,339 distinct ways, so that it is not too difficult to find a solution. But there are other interesting figures to be made; a 3×20 rectangle is not too difficult (there are two); and there are 65 ways of constructing a square 8×8 with the aid of one central 2×2 'tetromino'. The diagram (Fig. 16) shows a 10×6 rectangle and an 8×8 square. Other diversions with these pieces can readily be invented. They have a strange fascination.

2.2. THE CIRCLE

Practical models of the circle are of such everyday occurrence that there is no need to construct any special ones. In particular, the value of π can be calculated by measuring the length of a thread wound round a can, or the distance described by a bicycle wheel in a definite number of revolutions. Alternatively, knowing the value of π, the accuracy of the usual revolution-counter type of cyclometer can be tested. On the old 28-inch wheel, a speed of 5 m.p.h. gives almost exactly one tick per second; the modern 26-inch wheel gives slightly more.

It is possible to set up most of the geometrical theorems relating to the circle by means of a board on which a circle is painted, with tacks or gimp-pins driven in at intervals round its circumference. Extra pins are provided at the centre and along tangents and secants; straight lines are made by looping elastic thread over the pins. This apparatus is widely used in America under the name of 'theorem-board'.

† See, for example, *Math. Gazette*, **24** (1940), 209.

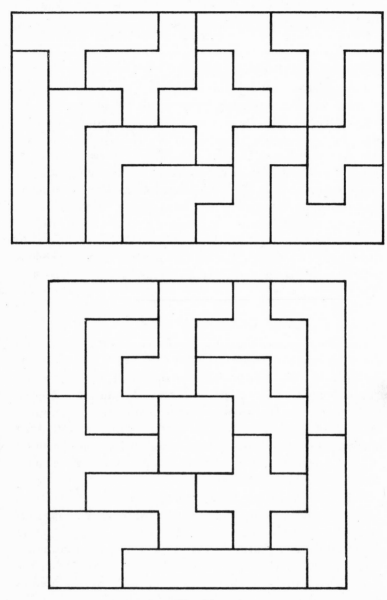

Fig. 16

A set square between two pins will demonstrate the constant angle property, but Fig. 17 illustrates a more ambitious device

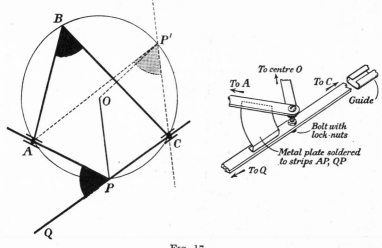

FIG. 17

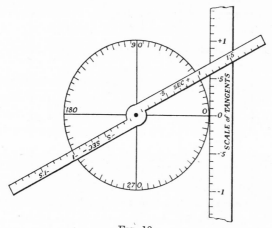

FIG. 18

which also shows the alternate segment property and the exterior angle of a cyclic quadrilateral; it is well worth the trouble involved in construction. The circle ABC and the lines AB, BC are painted on card which is then glued to a stout board. AP, OP, CP are movable rods, hinged at P and O and running in hinged guides at A and C. The rods are conveniently made of metal strip and the guides can be made from the flat joining sleeves for brass curtain rod. In order to enable the point P to pass through C (at which point the alternate segment theorem is shown) into the position indicated by dotted lines, the guide at C must have free travel down the whole rod CPQ. One way in which this can be arranged is shown. The guide must have a groove to take the lock-nut, or the latter must be recessed in the strip.

2.3. Circular Functions

There are several ways of showing the meaning of the three simple trigonometric functions. The easiest is probably the tangent, which comes first in many courses of study. A simple device can be made which shows the value of the ratio and the reason for its name (Fig. 18). Construct a circle divided into degrees, and a long strip hinged at the centre. With the radius as unit, mark off a uniform scale, positively and negatively, along the tangent at the zero of angles. The tangent of the angle to which the strip is turned can be read off from this scale. If a similar scale is marked on the rotating strip, the secant can be read off at the same time.

The sine and cosine take a little more trouble to demonstrate. One method involves the use of the angle in a semicircle (Fig. 19). A circular disk is pivoted about a point on its circumference so that it moves within a circle of twice its size. The sine and cosine can then be read off from the intersections of its rim with two perpendicular diameters of the fixed circle.

It makes the projections clearer, however, if the actual perpendiculars can be seen. For this purpose the semicircle is replaced by a rotating arrow carrying at its point a pivot on which two cross-wires, soldered at right angles, are fixed (Fig. 20). If a lead bob is attached to one of these and the whole is mounted vertically, the sine and cosine can be read off. These instruments have the great advantage of making clear the reasons for the sign conventions for the trigonometrical ratios of angles of any magnitude; also they lead easily to the use of

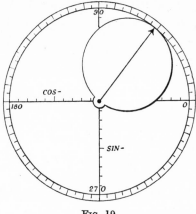

FIG. 19

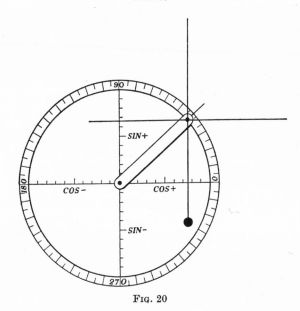

FIG. 20

coordinates and to the parametric form for the circle $x = a \cos \theta$, $y = a \sin \theta$. An instrument of this kind is shown in Plate 4a.

2.4. LOCI AND ENVELOPES

Though not strictly 'models', since few of them require any apparatus beyond the usual instruments, a set of well-drawn loci and envelopes adds greatly to the effectiveness of a mathematical exhibition. It will not therefore be out of place to include a short section on the subject. (It could of course be argued that any drawing is a 'model'.)

2.4.1. Simple loci. As examples of loci plotted pointwise by geometrical construction the following may be included:

Bipolar loci
$$
\begin{cases}
\text{The circle of Apollonius} & r = kr'. \\
\text{The ellipse and hyperbola} & r \pm r' = \text{constant.} \\
\text{Cassini's ovals} & rr' = \text{constant.} \\
\text{Cartesian ovals (2.4.3)} & r + kr' = \text{constant.}
\end{cases}
$$

The parabola, from the definition $SP = PM$.

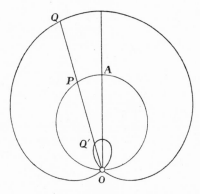

Fig. 21

The cardioid and limaçons, plotted by making PQ constant (positive or negative) on the variable secant OPQ (Fig. 21). The cardioid results when $PQ = OA$, the open limaçon when $PQ > OA$, and the limaçon with a node when $PQ < OA$.

The cissoid, obtained by cutting off $OX = PR$ (Fig. 22).

The conchoids are the curves $r = a \sec \theta + b$. They are obtained by drawing secants through O to meet a fixed line BAB' at R (see Fig. 23). If $OA = a$, and constant lengths

$$RY = RZ = b$$

are cut off from the secant, the loci of Y and Z together form the conchoid. Different members of the family obtained by varying the value of b can be drawn in the same figure. For $b = a$

the conchoid is the conchoid of Nicomedes, and has a cusp at O. If $b > a$, there is a loop.

The limaçons are obtained by a similar construction, replacing the line BAB' by the circle on OA as diameter. The secant

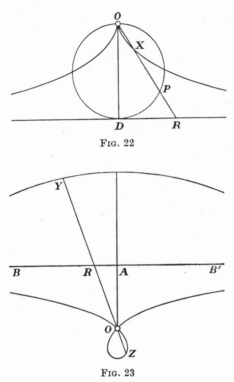

FIG. 22

FIG. 23

OR is extended each way by a length b as before. The equation of the resulting locus is $r = a \cos \theta + b$. When $b = a$, the curve has a cusp and is the cardioid; when $b < a$, there is a loop.

2.4.2. Loci using apparatus. A number of loci are most easily drawn continuously with the aid of special apparatus. There is no need for this to be unduly complicated: for example, the cycloid can be drawn by a piece of chalk attached to a tin-lid which is rolled along a ruler. Similar methods can be used to produce trochoids and epicycloids.

In the case of epicycloids it helps to have a slightly more

elaborate apparatus in which a link connects the centres of the rolling and fixed circles, and an endless thread in the form of a figure 8 passes round the disks to prevent slipping (Fig. 24).

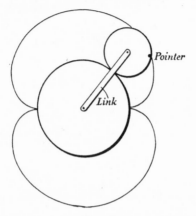

Fɪɢ. 24

The ellipse can be drawn with a Trammel of Archimedes— a pointer attached to a rod whose ends slide in perpendicular grooves—or, most simply, with a loop of thread enclosing the pencil point and two fixed pins. An elegant refinement of this latter method is as follows. Mount the pins on a board attached to a horizontal axle so that it can be rotated in a vertical plane. Replace the pencil point by an eye from which a bob hangs. As the board is rotated, the eye describes the ellipse (Fig. 25). If, in addition, a short horizontal tangent is attached to the eye, the law of equal angles is demonstrated and shown to be derivable from statical principles.

Conics can also be drawn by Newton's method, which depends on the properties of projective pencils. Two angles of constant magnitude are hinged at their vertices (Fig. 26). If one point of intersection is made to describe a line, the other will describe part of a conic. The proof of this depends on a basic result in projective geometry, but it is often useful to let coming events cast their shadows before. (To draw a complete curve requires trammels passing through the vertices of the angles.)

A great many curves can be drawn with simple linkages.

A full discussion of these is reserved for Chapter V, to which the reader is referred.

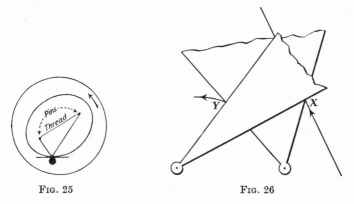

FIG. 25   FIG. 26

2.4.3. The Cartesian ovals. These are the curves given by the bipolar equation $r \pm kr' = $ constant. Each curve consists of a pair of ovals, one inside the other, but only one can be described with a positive value of k. If k is rational with small numerator and denominator, the curve can be described with pins and thread. The curves have the interesting property of possessing a third focus; i.e. there are three points in a line such that the equation of the curve referred to any two of them is of the form $r \pm kr' = c$, with different values of k and c according to which pair of foci is chosen.[†]

Fig. 27 shows a convenient set of ratios for which all three foci may be shown. $F_1 F_2 = 4$ units, $F_2 F_3 = 1$ unit. The equation referred to $F_1 F_3$ is $r_1 + 4r_3 = 10$; referred to $F_2 F_3$ it is $r_2 + 2r_3 = 4$. (The equation connecting r_1 and r_2 is $r_1 - 2r_2 = 2$, and cannot be demonstrated with looped thread, since it involves a negative k.) The other two equations can be demonstrated as in the figure. The threads are looped through rings at P, Q, and F_3. With persuasion and, preferably, nylon thread, each ring will be found to describe the same oval.

It is possible to demonstrate all three equations with the aid of an axle mounted behind the board as shown in the diagram. The strings must be initially adjusted so that P is on the oval;

† See, e.g., R. C. Lyness, *Math. Gazette*, **36** (1952), 315, note 2270.

the parts of the axle have diameters in the ratio $4:2:1$, and the strings are wound in the sense indicated, so that $\dot{r}_1 = -4\dot{r}_3$, $\dot{r}_2 = -2\dot{r}_3$, $\dot{r}_1 = 2\dot{r}_2$, and P describes the oval if the strings are maintained taut.

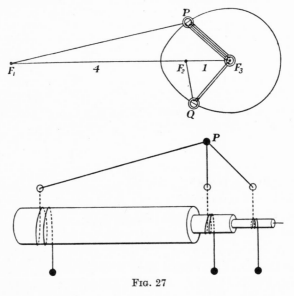

FIG. 27

Another possible set of equations is $r_2+2r_3 = 9$, $r_1+3r_3 = 16$, $2r_1-3r_2 = 5$ with $F_1F_2 = 5$, $F_2F_3 = 3$. Here the axles must have diameters in the ratio $3:2:1$.

A list of equations of miscellaneous loci is given at the end of this chapter.

2.4.4. Envelopes. A well-drawn envelope is much more attractive than a locus. In addition it is usually much easier to draw, since comparatively few ruled lines yield a reasonable result. It is the more surprising that so little attention is usually paid to envelopes. Some of the more simple examples are illustrated here.

The *ellipse* and *hyperbola* are obtained as negative pedals of a circle; i.e. the envelopes of PQ, where S is fixed, P moves on a fixed circle, and the angle SPQ is a right angle. (Figs. 28, 29.) The ellipse results when S is inside, and the hyperbola when S is outside the circle. (If S is on the circle the envelope is the

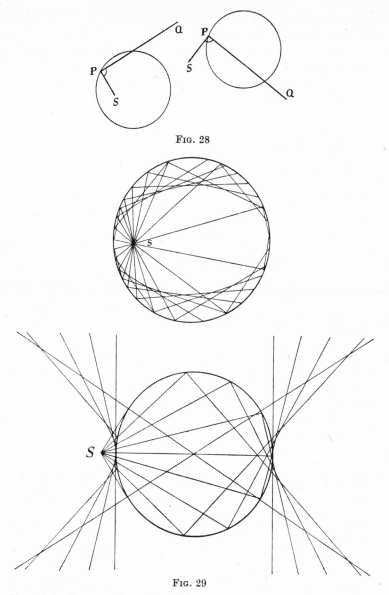

Fig. 28

Fig. 29

diametrically opposite point.) The two asymptotes to the hyperbola are the diameters perpendicular to the tangents from S to the circle.

The *parabola* is obtained in the same way when P moves along the fixed straight line XY (Figs. 30, 31).

These envelopes can also be obtained by paper-folding (see 2.7.3 below).

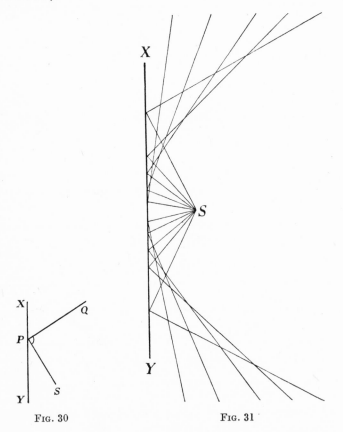

FIG. 30   FIG. 31

The *astroid*, or four-cusped hypocycloid, is the envelope of a line of constant length whose ends move on two perpendicular lines. In other words, it is the curve enveloped by the sliding ladder (Fig. 33). Since the instantaneous centre for the rod's motion is at I (Fig. 32), the point of contact of the rod with its envelope is at N, the foot of the perpendicular from I to the line. It is an interesting exercise to prove that the locus of N is the four-cusped hypocycloid formed by rolling the circle

IKN on the inside of the circle with centre *O* and radius
OI = LM.

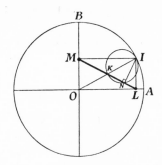

FIG. 32

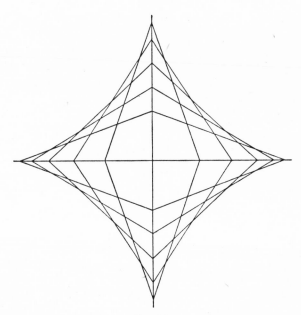

FIG. 33

The *deltoid*, or three-cusped hypocycloid, occurs as the envelope of the pedal (or Simson's) line of a variable point on the
circumcircle of a triangle (Fig. 34). To obtain it by constructing
these lines calls for careful drawing. It is simpler to use a
construction which can be used for any epi- or hypo-cycloid.

Draw a circle, which will be the *circumcircle* for an *epicycloid* and the *incircle* for a *hypocycloid*. Divide it into a large number n of equal arcs, say $n = 36$, or, for a curve with several cusps,

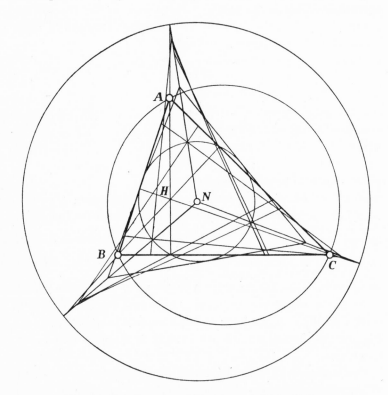

Fig. 34. The Deltoid as Envelope of Simson's Line

ABC is the triangle, *N* the nine-point centre, and *H* the orthocentre. The altitudes are the pedal lines of the vertices and the sides those of the diametrically opposite points. In addition to these six lines, and the three pedal lines of the points where the altitudes meet the circumcircle, the tangents to the deltoid from points at intervals of 30° on the circumference of the nine-point circle are shown in the figure.

$n = 72$. Number the points obtained from 0 upwards. An epicycloid with $(k-1)$ cusps is obtained as the envelope of the chords joining 1 to k, 2 to $2k$, 3 to $3k$, etc., the multiples being reduced modulo n. A hypocycloid with $k+1$ cusps is obtained by joining 1 to $-k$ (again mod n), 2 to $-2k$, etc., and producing the resulting secants. This will need more care in drawing and in the initial marking out.

The *nephroid* can be drawn by this means as a two-cusped epicycloid. This is the familiar curve seen in the tea-cup on a sunny day, i.e. the 'caustic by reflection' for rays of light reflected in a semicircular mirror.

If such a mirror is available, it makes a very pretty pattern if a beam of light is passed through a set of parallel narrow slits—for example, a comb, or a glass plate on which thin strips of passe-partout have been gummed. Mount the mirror with its axis parallel to the

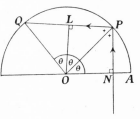

FIG. 35

rays so formed, and the caustic with its enveloping rays will be clearly seen on a shaded background. To show that it is indeed the epicycloid, notice (Fig. 35) that if $\widehat{AOP} = \theta$, then $\widehat{OPN} = \widehat{OPL} = \widehat{OQL} = \frac{1}{2}\pi - \theta$, so that $\widehat{POL} = \widehat{QOL} = \theta$ and $\widehat{AOQ} = 3\theta$. Thus the envelope is obtained by joining the points $p, 3p$ in the above construction. The actual caustic runs only from $\theta = 0$ to $\theta = \pi$, giving half the nephroid, and is shown in Fig. 36, but the full curve is obtained by continuing from $\theta = \pi$ to 2π.

The *cardioid* is the epicycloid with one cusp; it can be obtained as an envelope by the above construction: as a locus as the *conchoid* of a circle—draw chords from a fixed point of the circle and extend them a distance equal to the diameter of the circle: or it can be drawn by a linkage described in Chapter V. It is the reflexion caustic of a circle when the source of light is on the circumference, as is easily shown.

There are, finally, the projective envelopes obtained by joining points of homographic ranges; the simplest is the parabola obtained by joining points of congruent ranges, say $(p, 0)$ to $(0, k-p)$ for fixed k, the axes being not necessarily rectangular. Further, in the circle described above, the chords joining 0 to p and k to $k-p$, for fixed k and variable p, meet on a rectangular hyperbola. This latter curve is more easily obtained as the envelope (and locus of mid-point) of the line joining $(p, 0)$ to $(0, k/p)$ on rectangular axes.

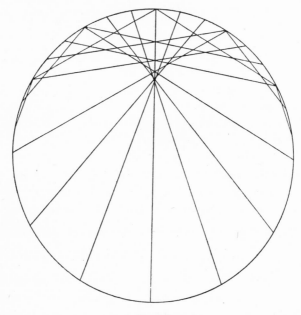

FIG. 36

2.4.5. Circular envelopes.

When the parabola is drawn, we construct the circles with centres on the curve and which pass through the vertex; they envelop the *cissoid* (Fig. 37). In a similar manner if we construct the circles with centres on the rectangular hyperbola and passing through its centre, the resulting envelope is the *Lemniscate of Bernoulli* (Fig. 38); a result as unexpected as it is pleasing.

In general the envelope of circles through a fixed point with centres on a given curve is a curve similar to the *pedal* of the given curve with respect to the given point. For example, if the given curve is a circle, the envelope will be a *limaçon*, and in particular, if the point is on the circle, a *cardioid*.

A further circular envelope worth drawing is the envelope of circles on parallel chords of a fixed circle as diameter; it is

FIG. 37

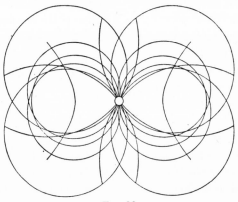

FIG. 38

an ellipse with additional circles converging towards its foci, and in fact is the flattened plane form of the model discussed in 4.3.6.

2.5. CURVE-STITCHING

One very old method of expression work in mathematics, and one which affords a welcome change from 'the tyranny of

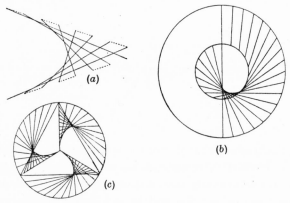

FIG. 39

pencil and paper', is that of curve-stitching. It seems to have originated in a book by Mrs. E. L. Somervell, entitled *A Rhythmic Approach to Mathematics*, published in 1906 and now long out of print. The idea has recently been revived, both in America and in this country. Basically it consists of constructing straight-line envelopes by stitching with coloured threads through a pattern of holes pricked in cardboard. Small children and quite advanced geometers can find in this work a satisfying form of expression. Beginners of course must have their patterns ready-made; but very little knowledge is required to enable pupils to construct their own.

The simplest patterns are obtained by joining holes which are equally spaced on straight lines or circles. In the case of two straight lines the resulting envelope is the parabola. More complicated curves result from the use of circles.

The designs in Figs. 39 (a)–(c) are reproduced from Mrs. Somervell's book; an endless variety of modifications can of course be made. The one rule which must invariably be followed is that on the reverse side of the card the thread is always taken to the adjacent hole on the pattern (as indicated in Fig. 39 (*a*), by dotted lines); on the right side the thread goes across to the next unoccupied hole on the far side of the design.

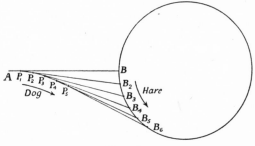

FIG. 40

Once the fundamental idea of the method has been mastered, anyone interested can construct his own designs. Exact algebraic curves will usually need unequal spacing of the holes and therefore more calculation will be required to produce them; it is surprising, however, what a variety of beautiful figures can be executed which are based on the simple principle of equal spacing.

The curve of pursuit is another possibility worked out by the originator of the method. This has the disadvantage that the holes for the stitches cannot be pricked beforehand, but it is in a way an advantage that the curve 'grows' as the stitches are made with all the fascination of a new discovery.

For example, suppose a dog chases a hare running on a circular track. An approximate curve of pursuit is stitched as follows (approximate because it is formed in finite steps instead of by a continuous process—a difference which introduces the idea of a limit). Suppose the dog is at A and the hare at B (Fig. 40). Stitch AB to represent the dog's intention. With dividers set to a fixed length mark off AP_1 along the stitch, and with the same interval, or with a fixed multiple of it, mark off BB_2 along the circle. The next stitch returns on the underside to P_1 and goes from P_1 to B_2 (the dog's new intention). Then

$P_1 P_2$, $B_2 B_3$ are marked off and the stitch returns to P_2 and then from P_2 to B_3, and so on. This is more difficult to execute than the parabola, but interesting curves are obtained.

2.6. ROULETTES AND INVOLUTES

2.6.1. A *roulette* is the curve generated by a point which is carried by a curve which rolls on a fixed curve. Particular

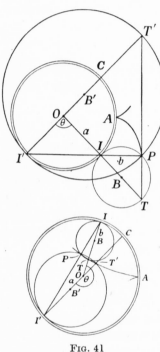

examples follow. The locus of a point carried by a circle rolling on a straight line is a *trochoid*. If the point is inside the circle the trochoid has inflexions; if it is outside the circle, but rigidly attached to it, the trochoid has loops. This is the answer to the old catch-question, 'Which parts of a train are moving in the opposite direction to the train as a whole?' In the particular case when the point is on the circumference of the rolling circle the roulette is a *cycloid*. When the circle rolls on the outside of another circle the corresponding curves are the *epitrochoids* and *epicycloids*; if it rolls on the inside, they are the *hypotrochoids* and *hypocycloids*. Methods of

FIG. 41

drawing these curves as loci or envelopes have been discussed in 2.4.

2.6.2. It is interesting to see that epicycloids and hypocycloids can be described as roulettes in two ways: in the case of the hypocycloid by rolling circles of radii b, $(a-b)$ inside a circle of radius a; and in the case of the epicycloid by rolling a circle of radius b on a circle of radius a, or by rolling a circle of radius $(a+b)$ so as to enclose the fixed circle of radius a. This is shown in Fig. 41.

Suppose P is a point on the roulette, and let a be the radius of the fixed circle, centre O (drawn with a double line). The centre of the rolling circle is B and its radius b. Let I be the point of contact. Produce PI to I', and let $I'O$ meet TP, the tangent to the roulette, at T' and the fixed circle at C. The circle on $I'T'$ as diameter passes through P, since $I'PT'$ is a right angle (PII' is normal to the roulette), and touches the fixed circle at I'. Also since IC is perpendicular to II' and therefore parallel to PT', $ITT'C$ is an isosceles trapezium and

$$CT' = IT = 2b.$$

Hence the radius of this third circle is $(a+b)$ for the epicycloid and $(a-b)$ for the hypocycloid. Thus, if B' is the centre of the circle $I'PT'$,

$$OB' = b = BP \quad \text{and} \quad B'P = a \pm b = OB,$$

so that $OB'PB$ is a parallelogram and $B'P$ is parallel to OI.

Finally, in the upper figure,

$$\text{arc } I'P = (a+b)\theta = a\theta + b\theta = \text{arc } I'I + \text{arc } IP$$
$$= \text{arc } I'I + \text{arc } IA = \text{arc } I'A;$$

and in the lower figure

$$\text{major arc } I'P = (a-b)\theta = a\theta - b\theta$$
$$= \text{major arc } I'I - \text{major arc } IP$$
$$= \text{major arc } I'I - \text{arc } IA = \text{arc } I'A.$$

Hence in each case the roulette is also generated by the rolling of the circle centre B' on the same fixed circle.

A model to show this is difficult to make successfully on account of friction. In the case of the hypocycloid the fixed circle can be a circular inlay in a board, in which rotate two thin circular disks, hinged together at P. Their centres are pivoted on short links OB, OB' which attach them to an axle at O. An elevation of the arrangement is shown in Fig. 42. The disks can be rimmed with felt to provide adequate grip.

In the case of the epicycloid the small circle can be attached as described in 2.4 (Fig. 24), with an endless thread surrounding it and the fixed wheel, but the large circle presents difficulty as, unless it is made solid, a link OB' cannot be attached, but then the movement cannot be seen. The large wheel must either be spoked, or better still, made of 'Perspex' which will allow the motion to be observed through it.

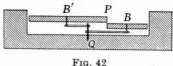

FIG. 42

If any epicycloid is rolled on a line, the centre of the fixed circle describes an ellipse.

2.6.3. By a theorem in kinematics, any 'trammel' curve, or curve described by a linkage, is a roulette described by the carried point when the body-locus of the instantaneous centre of the carrier link rolls on its space-locus. For example, the path of any point of a rod whose ends slide on two fixed lines (a 'trammel of Archimedes') is an ellipse; the motion is that of a circle with the rod as diameter rolling on the inside of a fixed circle of twice the size. This matter will be taken up again in Chapter V.

An interesting chain of roulettes is the following. Roll a straight line on a circle; any point of the line describes an involute of the circle, discussed in 2.6.4 below. Roll the involute, still attached to the circle, on a line; the centre of the circle describes a parabola. Roll the parabola on a line; the focus describes a *catenary* (the curve formed by a hanging chain; see 5.1.5).

The roulettes described by the foci of the conics in general when rolled upon a line are the sections of the minimal surfaces known as *unduloids*; see, for example, D'Arcy Thompson, *On Growth and Form*, p. 368, fig. 104. These surfaces are special cases of the forms taken up by a soap film spanning the space between prescribed boundaries. The surface formed by rotating the catenary itself is called the *catenoid*, and is the shape of a film stretched between two circular wires in parallel planes, with their centres on an axis normal to their planes.

The general problem of finding the surface of least area

spanning a given contour is known as Plateau's problem, after the nineteenth-century physicist who studied it in detail. The theoretical solution is very complicated, but in practice an approximation to any particular solution can be obtained by taking a wire frame in the shape of the contour and dipping it in a solution of soap mixed with glycerine. Many very beautiful surfaces can be obtained in this way, especially if the wire frame is in the form of a regular polyhedron or one of the knots described in 2.8 below, or even two linked circles.

2.6.4. Involutes. If a string is attached to a point of a curve, lying along the tangent to the curve at that point, and is 'wrapped up' on to the curve, the locus of any point of the string is an *involute* of the given curve. It can be proved that the point of contact of the string at any instant is the centre of curvature of the involute at the corresponding point: the original curve is the *evolute* of the involute; i.e. the locus of its centres of curvature, or the envelope of its normals (see Fig. 43).

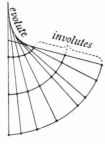

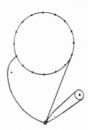

FIG. 43   FIG. 44

Involutes can be drawn very easily by mechanical means. For example, we may draw the involute of a circle, one of the most important members of the class. A circle is drawn on a sheet of paper which is then placed on a wooden board or a cork base, and pins are driven in at regular and reasonably close intervals along its circumference. A thread is tied to one of the pins, and a pencil-point is placed in a loop at the other end of the thread (Fig. 44). As the thread is wound or unwound from the circle of pins the pencil traces out part of the involute. This curve is also the locus of a point of a straight edge which rolls on the circle—e.g. a point on a see-saw consisting of a straight plank on a cylindrical log.

Alternatively the pencil-point can be replaced by a bob, and the whole board mounted as described in 2.4.2 (Fig. 25). This is a suitable treatment for any of the following involutes.

One involute of a cycloid is an equal cycloid. In Fig. 45 the thread $OP = $ arc OM, half the arch of the cycloid, or twice the diameter of the rolling circle. This fact was made use of by Huygens in designing the cycloidal pendulum, which has a period strictly independent of the amplitude. There are other more serious sources of error than this in the pendulum clock, and nowadays steps are taken instead to maintain a constant amplitude with a simpler suspension.

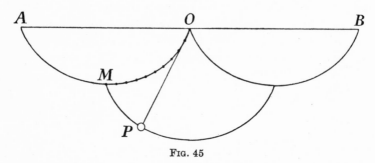

Fig. 45

In general, the evolute of any epi- or hypo-cycloid is a similar curve rotated through an angle. In the case of the cardioid the evolute is $\frac{1}{3}$ the size; for the nephroid the factor is $\frac{1}{2}$, for the deltoid 3, and for the astroid 2.

The cardioid (Fig. 46) gives a particularly pleasing demonstration. The same method can of course be used for the conics, but only part of the curve can be drawn; one-half of the ellipse, less than a quarter of the hyperbola, and part of one-half of the parabola (Fig. 47). In this case the evolute is a semi-cubical parabola, similar to $y^2 = x^3$.

2.6.5. The tractrix. This curve is an involute of a catenary described by a point which is initially at the vertex of the curve. Fig. 48 shows the geometrical relationships involved. Ox is the directrix of the catenary $y = c \cosh(x/c)$; PQ is the

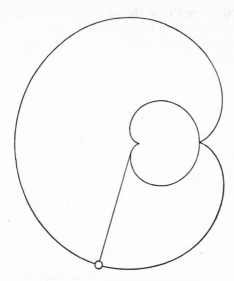

FIG. 46

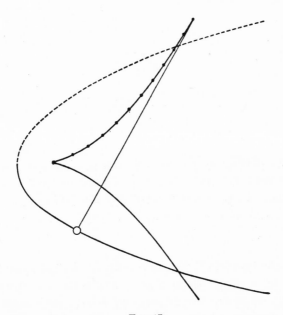

FIG. 47

tangent at P, and $PQ = $ arc PC, so that Q is a point of the involute. The well-known equations for the catenary, $s = c \tan \psi$,
$y^2 = s^2 + c^2$, show that RQ is perpendicular to PQ and

$$RQ = c = CO.$$

Thus the locus of Q is the curve traced out by the end of a string
of fixed length c, initially lying along OC, when the other end,

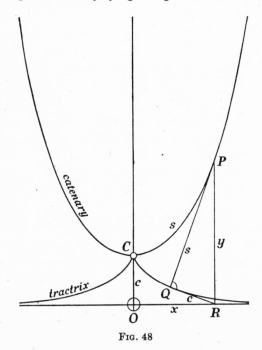

FIG. 48

O, is moved along the line Ox. This is the origin of the name
'tractrix'. If a small flat weight is attached to the string the
locus can be demonstrated by placing the weight on a flat board
and dragging the other end slowly along the fixed line.

The tractrix has the property that the surface of revolution
formed by rotating it about the asymptote Ox has constant
negative Gauss curvature, and for this reason is known as the
pseudosphere. Triangles drawn on it have the sum of their
angles less than 180°. It is one of the models which have
properties analogous to the 'hyperbolic' plane of Lobachewski.

2.6.6. Involute gears. An important practical application of the involute of a circle is in the construction of gear-teeth. These were made at one time in the form of epi- and hypocycloids. Imagine two circles touching one another, concentric with the gear-wheels, with radii in the same ratio as the gear-ratio required. If a small circle rolls on the outside of one of

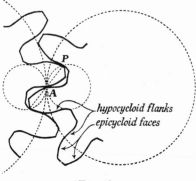

hypocycloid flanks
epicycloid faces

FIG. 49

these circles and on the inside of the other, two cycloids, one epi- and one hypo-, will be described by a point of the small circle, and these curves will remain in contact as the original circles roll on one another. For at any instant both cycloids pass through the same point P of the small circle which touches the large circles at their point of contact A; and each curve has PA as normal at this instant. The curves therefore slide upon one another. Thus we can construct the projecting 'faces' of the gear teeth as epicycloids provided we construct the indented 'flanks' on the other gear-wheel as the corresponding hypocycloids (see Fig. 49).

This method of construction has the disadvantage that the distance between the centres of the gears must be exactly equal to that which was assumed in calculating the form of the teeth; otherwise the velocity-ratio transmitted is not constant. Also the teeth are difficult to cut accurately, and they tend to wear unevenly.

To overcome these disadvantages the involute tooth was

invented. Consider two circles concentric with the gear-wheels, with radii in the same ratio as the gear-ratio as before, but not now in contact. Draw their internal common tangents (see Fig. 50). If a string is passed round the circles and crossed over between them it will lie along these common tangents, and,

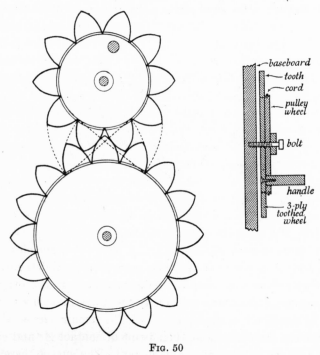

Fig. 50

provided it does not slip, a constant velocity-ratio will be transmitted no matter what the distance between the centres of the circles. The locus of any point of the part of the string which is moving along one of the tangents, *considered relative to a plane carried by either rotating circle*, is an involute of that circle. These two involutes remain in contact *at the same point of the string* (a variable point of the tangent) as the circles rotate. Thus two gear-teeth, one on each circle, whose faces are these two involutes, will remain in contact and transmit a constant velocity ratio. The complete teeth can now be constructed as in the diagram. (The teeth need not come to a point, nor need opposite faces meet in cusps on the circumference, but the diagram has been so drawn for simplicity.)

To make a model, cut flat disks of diameter equal to the overall diameter of the toothed wheel required. Choose a simple gear-ratio and plot out carefully the points and cusps of the teeth on each disk. Plywood is a suitable material as the teeth are easily cut with a fret-saw. The teeth can be marked out with a template before cutting. To plot the involute for this purpose it is sufficient to use the compass, taking successive centres along the circumference and increasing the radius by small steps.

Mount the plywood disks on solid wooden pulley wheels, grooved to take a cord, the diameters of the grooves being exactly those of the base circles of the involutes. Fit the gears together so that they revolve easily without backlash and bolt them to a base-board. A handle can be provided in one of the disks. Care should be taken to cut sufficient teeth to ensure a constant drive; the diagram is on the border line in this respect. The model demonstrates clearly the constant velocity-ratio, as the cord does not slip.

If desired, a model of cycloidal gears can be made similarly, but the teeth are not easy to cut accurately; a good reason for the supersession of this type of tooth. Rack-and-pinion teeth can be constructed in a similar way; the faces and flanks in the case of the rack-teeth will now be ordinary cycloids.

2.7. PAPER-FOLDING

This is another method which has possibilities which have been more fully explored in America (see *Geometrical Exercises in Paper Folding* by T. Sundara Row; also the article by R. C. Yates in *The 18th Yearbook of the National Council of Teachers of Mathematics*, p. 154).

2.7.1. Triangle. If a triangle is cut out of paper, it is easy by suitable folding to obtain as creases

    (*a*) the perpendicular bisectors of the sides (vertex on vertex);

    (*b*) the altitudes;

(c) the angle-bisectors (side on side);

(d) the medians, after (a) has been done.

The concurrence of each of these four sets of creases can be demonstrated in this way.

2.7.2. Another use of paper-folding has been mentioned in 2.1.2 above. See also 3.14, plaited polyhedra.

2.7.3. Conics. These can be described as envelopes of creases if a circle is drawn on the paper. Tracing paper, or thin wax-paper (jam-pot covers) should be used. To obtain the ellipse, mark a point P inside the circle, and fold so that P falls on the circumference of the circle. The envelope of the creases so obtained will be an ellipse with one focus at P.

To obtain the hyperbola, P must be taken outside the circle.

If P lies on the circle, the result is not a parabola, but a single point, the centre of the circle. To obtain the parabola a line l and a point P outside it must be marked. The paper is then folded so as to bring P on l; the creases formed will envelop a parabola with P as focus and l as directrix.

2.7.4. Polygonal knots. If a strip of paper is knotted once and carefully pressed flat the folds will form a regular pentagon (Fig. 51 (a)). All polygons with an odd number of sides may be produced in this way; the knot which produces the heptagon is shown in Fig. 51 (b). The even-sided polygons require two strips of equal width; a reef-knot leads to the hexagon, Fig. 51 (c). To make the octagon, Fig. 51 (d), it is best to begin by knotting and pressing one strip only, as in Fig. 51 (e). The complete octagon consists of two such knots interlinked.

2.8. KNOTS

Mathematically speaking, a *knot* is a simple closed curve in three-dimensional space. Both in a plane and also in space of four dimensions all such curves can be deformed, without crossing themselves, into simple circles; but in three dimensions there is the possibility of the curve forming a knot which cannot be so deformed. The study and classification of knots involves advanced analysis and mathematical difficulties of a high order. Even the simplest cases are by no means easily treated, and a few examples are given here. Models are easily made of string, or better, of plastic tubing which can be joined by pushing the

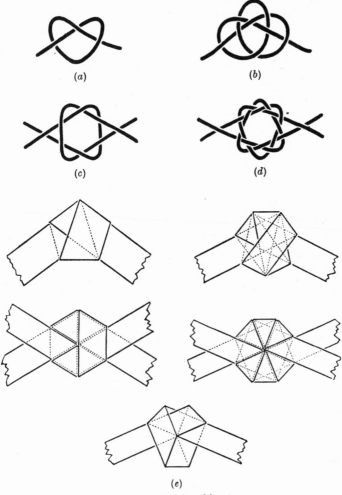

(a)

(b)

(c)

(d)

(e)

FIG. 51. Polygonal knots

ends over match-sticks or old gramophone needles, without unsightly knots.

The simplest knots are the two 'clover' knots, forming an 'enantiomorphic' pair (Fig. 52 (a)); i.e. each is the mirror-image of the other. It is no mean task to prove by abstract methods that one cannot be deformed into the other, but a little mani-

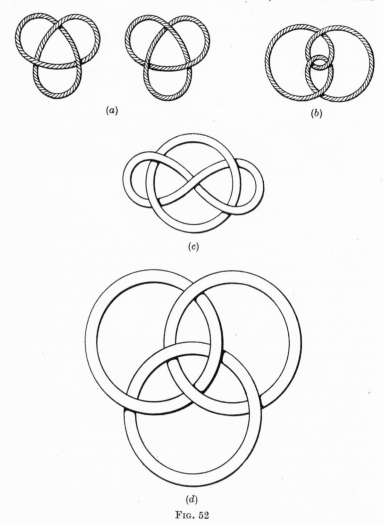

(a)

(b)

(c)

(d)

Fig. 52

pulation will readily convince anyone that this deformation is impossible.

The next simplest is the knot with four crossings shown in Fig. 52 (b). This is 'amphicheiral', i.e. it can be deformed into its mirror-image, unlike the two clover-knots. (Amphicheiral = fitting either hand; socks are amphicheiral, but shoes and gloves are not.) There are two kinds of knot with five crossings (alternately over and under); after that the number rises rapidly. Some of the difficulties of the subject are illustrated by the linked loops in Fig. 52 (c). Each loop by itself can be deformed into an open circle—it is not knotted. The loops do not enclose one another like links of a chain, yet they cannot be disentangled. It may not be immediately obvious without a model that the configuration is symmetrical in the two loops. The reader may or may not be edified to learn that the locking of these two curves is expressed analytically in its simplest form by the relation

$$x^{-1}y^{-1}x^{-1}yxyx^{-1}y^{-1}xyxy^{-1}x^{-1}y^{-1}xy = 1,$$

where x, y are the operations of threading, in a fixed sense, each of the two loops. The linkage has assumed considerable importance in some recondite theorems of topology.

The three rings shown in Fig. 52 (d) are such that no two are linked together but all three are; cutting any one frees the other two. They derive their name 'Borromean' from the fact of their forming the arms of the Italian family of Borromeo; they are also the trade-mark of an American liquor manufacturer, in whose gaily-coloured advertisements they appear.

2.9. PLANE TESSELLATIONS

A convenient link between plane diagrams and solid configurations is provided by the study of plane tessellations. They form a suitable introduction to the polyhedra and their nets considered in the next chapter. In fact a plane tessellation is the special case of an infinite polyhedron.

2.9.1. The three regular tessellations. A regular tessellation is a pattern of congruent regular polygons, all of one kind, filling the whole plane.

It is evident, by considering angles at a point, that only squares, equilateral triangles, and hexagons are admissible, and these do in fact give three regular tessellations. The pattern of squares is familiar enough; the chess-board and a sheet of squared paper are obvious examples. The hexagons can be seen in the honeycomb, in patchwork cushions, and in wire-netting. The triangles are rather less frequently met with: many orchards are planted in this pattern (Fig. 53); graph-paper so ruled is called isometric paper.

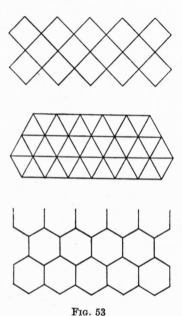

FIG. 53

2.9.2. The semi-regular tessellations. Although many designs can be based on the three regular patterns, in themselves they are not of great interest, except perhaps as an introduction to the five regular polyhedra. The scope and interest of these patterns is enormously increased if we consider the so-called semi-regular tessellations now to be described. These correspond in the plane to the semi-regular Archimedean solids in space which we shall describe in the next chapter.

It is convenient to anticipate the notation there used for these solids, which is equally applicable to the plane tessellations. This is the modified *Schläfli symbol*. A facially-regular solid or tessellation is a set of regular polygons of two or more kinds so arranged that every vertex is congruent to every other

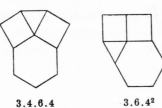

3.4.6.4   3.6.4²

Fig. 54

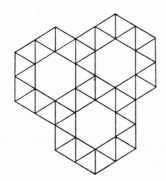

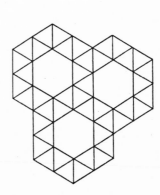

3⁴.6

Fig. 55

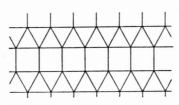

3³.4²

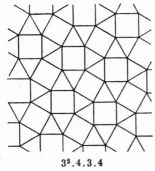

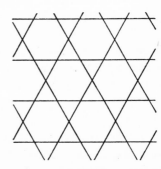

3².4.3.4   3.6.3.6

Fig. 56

vertex. The whole figure is then completely specified by giving the polygons occurring at any vertex in the order in which they are found. This information is abbreviated in a single symbol: thus $3^4.5$ means that at every vertex there are four contiguous equilateral triangles and one regular pentagon (this is an

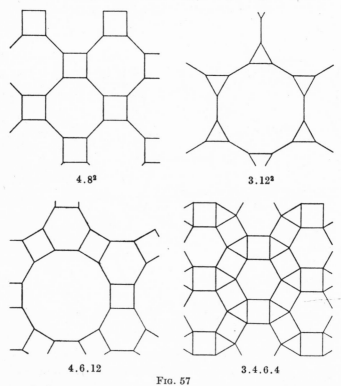

4.8²   3.12²

4.6.12   3.4.6.4
Fig. 57

Archimedean solid, the snub dodecahedron). $3^4.6$ means four triangles and one hexagon at each vertex—a plane tessellation. 3.4.6.4 would be distinct from 3.6.4² as shown in Fig. 54. Of these, 3.4.6.4 extends to a complete tessellation; 3.6.4² does not.

It can be shown that there are eight semi-regular plane tessellations, and no more. Their symbols are $3^3.4^2$, $3^2.4.3.4$, 3.6.3.6, $3^4.6$, 3.12², 4.8², 4.6.12, 3.4.6.4. (The regular tessellations in this notation are 3^6, 6^3, 4^4.) One of these, $3^4.6$, has two forms which are mirror-images of one another (*enantiomorphic*); all the others are symmetrical. These forms cannot be brought into congruence without turning the plane over (Fig. 55).

When the tessellations are drawn they can be coloured or used as the basis of various designs. The manufacturers of

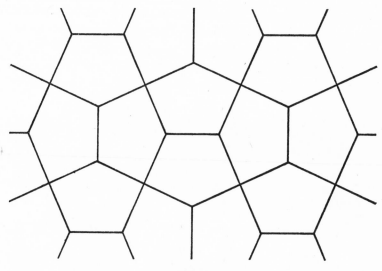

FIG. 58

linoleum appear to be familiar only with $3.6.3.6$ and 4.8^2; there ought to be a future awaiting a designer who bases his patterns on $3^4.6$ or $3^2.4.3.4$. Interesting colour schemes can be devised for all the tessellations, and suitable schemes help very much in bringing out the essential geometry of the pattern. For example, it will be found that $3^4.6$ is really $3.3.3^2.6$, since one set of triangles has no side in common with a hexagon and is differently related to the pattern from the other triangles. If this set (which forms a triangular pattern 3^6 on its own) is coloured differently, the meaning of the pattern is clarified.

Diagrams of all the tessellations are shown in Figs. 53–57.

2.9.3. Tiling patterns. Regular patterns of tiles can be based on any of these tessellations or on any of the various types

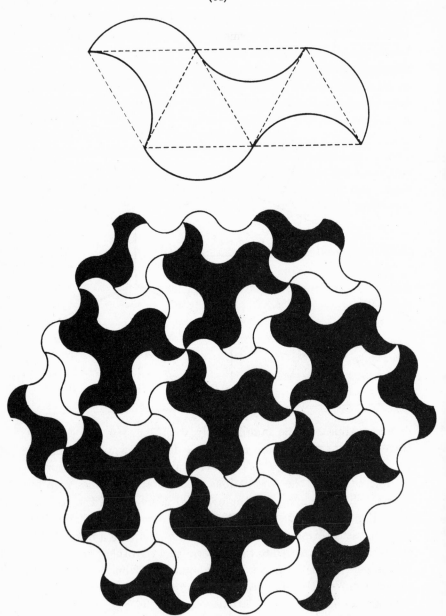

Fig. 59

of plane lattice, for example on the parallelogram or rhombus. Designers in this country do not seem to have been very enterprising in this respect. Star octagons are sometimes found, and rhombi of various angles. A full account of patterns can be found in MacMahon's *New Mathematical Pastimes*. We have space here for one of his; it consists of equal-sided (but not regular) pentagons, but has the appearance of interlocking hexagons (Fig. 58). Another design hails from Italy and appeared in the *Daily Telegraph* in 1955; it shows what can be done with a simple curved unit (Fig. 59). An artistically inclined mathematician can find plenty of scope for originality in designing repetitive patterns which can be mass-produced in tiles.

2.10. CURVES AS LIMITS OF POLYGONAL SEQUENCES

There are a number of curves of special interest which are defined as the limits of certain sequences of polygons, each figure being derived from the one before it in the sequence. These curves were invented to illustrate definite properties; for example that of finite area combined with infinite length. We shall mention three and show in diagrams the early terms of the sequences, in the hope that the reader will appreciate the beauty of their patterns and will feel that for that reason, if for no other, they are worth drawing.

2.10.1. The Von Koch 'snowflake' curve. Take an equilateral triangle C_0. Trisect each side, and replace the centre third of each by two sides of an equilateral triangle described on it outwards, thus obtaining C_1 (Fig. 60). Treat C_1 in the same way, obtaining C_2, and so on. Von Koch's curve is $C = \lim_{n \to \infty} C_n$. The reader may verify that if l_n, A_n are the length and area of C_n,

$$l_n = 3a \times \left(\frac{4}{3}\right)^n; \qquad A_n = A_{n-1} + \frac{1}{3} \frac{l_{n-1}}{a} \frac{\Delta}{3^n};$$

where a, Δ are the side and area of the original triangle C_0. Hence $l_n \to \infty$, $A_n \to \frac{8}{5}\Delta$. Thus C has infinite length, finite area, and at no point possesses a tangent.

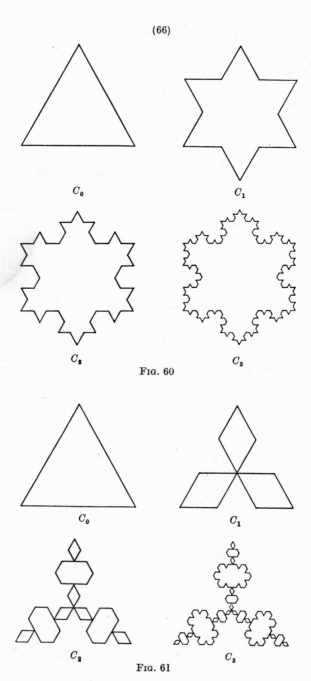

C_0

C_1

C_2

C_3

Fig. 60

C_0

C_1

C_2

C_3

Fig. 61

2.10.2. The 'anti-snowflake' curve is obtained as the limit of a similar sequence, the only difference being that the equilateral triangles are turned inwards instead of outwards. The first four terms are shown in Fig. 61. In this case l_n is the same as before, but

$$A_n = A_{n-1} - \frac{1}{3}\frac{l_{n-1}}{a}\frac{\Delta}{3^n},$$

and thus $A_\infty = \frac{2}{5}\Delta$. The curve has double-points at a 'Cantor-set' of points on the radii OA, OB, OC of the original triangle, formed by repeated trisection and rejection of the centre third.

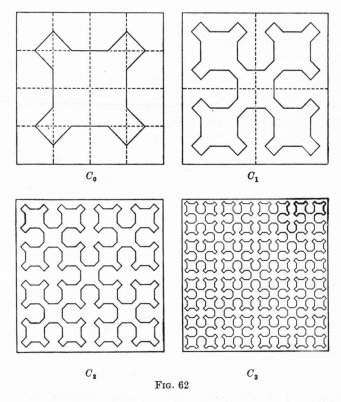

$$C_0 \qquad\qquad\qquad C_1$$

$$C_2 \qquad\qquad\qquad C_3$$

Fig. 62

2.10.3. The Sierpinski curve. This curve has the remarkable property that it contains every interior point of a square, yet it is unicursal and its 'area' is less than half that of the square. We begin with a square divided into sixteen smaller squares.

The vertices of C_0 are all mid-points of the edges of these squares, as shown in the diagram, Fig. 62. Divide the original square into four; in each corner construct a C_0 on half the scale, and unite them as shown in the centre, obtaining C_1. The diagram indicates sufficiently clearly how the process is repeated to obtain C_2, C_3,.... Sierpinski's curve $C = \lim_{n \to \infty} C_n$, as before.

If a is the side of the original square, the reader may verify that

$$l_0 = a\left(1 + \frac{3}{\sqrt{2}}\right); \qquad l_n = 2l_{n-1} + \frac{a}{4^n}\left(1 - \frac{1}{\sqrt{2}}\right);$$

$$l_n \to \infty.$$

$$A_0 = \frac{11a^2}{32}; \qquad A_n = A_{n-1} + \frac{7a^2}{32}\frac{1}{4^n};$$

$$A_\infty = \tfrac{5}{12}a^2.$$

It is also possible to carry out the sequence if C_0 consists of four squares on alternate sides of a regular octagon; in this case each polygon is a chain of sides of the Archimedean plane tessellation 4.8^2 (see 2.9.2):

$$l_0 = 8a(\sqrt{2} - 1); \qquad l_n = 2l_{n-1};$$

$$A_0 = \frac{a^2}{2}(5 - 3\sqrt{2}); \qquad A_n = A_{n-1} + a^2\frac{\sqrt{2} - 1}{2}\frac{1}{4^n};$$

$$A_\infty = \frac{a^2}{3}(7 - 4\sqrt{2}).$$

2.11. GOLDEN SECTION

This is of frequent occurrence in the various pentagonal polyhedra, and also has an interest of its own, so that there need be no excuse for introducing it here.

A line is said to be divided in golden section if the ratio of the whole line to the larger part is equal to the ratio of the larger to the smaller part. If this ratio is τ, we have $\tau^2 = \tau + 1$, so that

$$\tau = \frac{\sqrt{5} + 1}{2} = 1 \cdot 6180.$$

The connexion between this ratio and the pentagon can be seen as follows. Consider a triangle ABC with angles 36°, 72°, and 72°. Bisect one base-angle B, so forming two further triangles BCD, ABD, both isosceles.

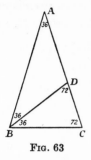
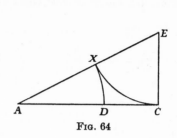

FIG. 63　　　　　　　　　　FIG. 64

Then $AD = BD = BC$, and from the similar triangles BDC, ABC

$$\frac{AD}{DC} = \frac{BC}{DC} = \frac{AC}{BC} = \frac{AC}{AD};$$

so that AC is divided at D in golden section. Thus if D can be found, $\triangle DBC$ can be constructed by making

$$DB = CB = DA,$$

and hence the angle of 72° and the regular pentagon can be constructed.

The geometrical construction for golden section is shown in Fig. 64, in which $\quad EX = EC = \frac{1}{2}AC.$

It is easy to show that

$$\frac{AD}{DC} = \tau.$$

If a rectangle is drawn with its sides in the ratio $\tau:1$, it has the property that the removal of a square from one end of the rectangle leaves a similar rectangle, turned through a right angle. If this process is continued a nest of squares is formed converging on a point O, which is the pole of an equiangular spiral which passes through A, F, G, H,..., the successive points of division (see Fig. 65). The angle of the spiral can be shown to be the root of the equation $\exp(\frac{1}{2}\pi \cot \phi) = \tau$, i.e. 73° very nearly. This figure is well worth constructing. If an attempt is made to draw it by measurement of the ratios, it will be found that errors are cumulative and the rectangles rapidly depart from the correct shape. This can be avoided by noting that the successive points of subdivision lie on the diagonals *BD*, *CE*, and the pole *O* of the spiral is where these two lines

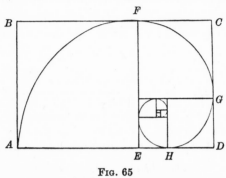

FIG. 65

intersect. The points of subdivision form an excellent example of a geometrical sequence with a limit-point. The circular quadrants form a close approximation to the true spiral, which almost touches the sides of the rectangles, since

$$O\widehat{F}C = \tan^{-1}\tau^3 = 76° 43'.$$

The lines *OA*, *OB*, *OF*, *OC*, *OG*, *OD*, etc., are at angles of 45°. The Greeks considered the rectangle of this shape to have the most beautiful proportions, and some of their temples are built on this plan. The spiral of this angle ϕ has been held to occur as a basis of many great paintings. It occurs also naturally in snail-shells and flower-heads, and in other places. See D'Arcy Thompson, *On Growth and Form*, chaps. xi and xiv.

To judge from the figures and statements in some of the literature, it has often been supposed that this spiral does in fact touch the sides at *A*, *F*, *G*, *H*, etc.† But this is not so, and such a spiral is impossible. The condition for two perpendicular tangents to be equal is

$$\exp(\tfrac{1}{2}\pi \cot \phi) = \tan(\tfrac{3}{4}\pi - \phi)$$

† But compare the footnote to fig. 360, p. 764, in D'Arcy Thompson, op. cit.

for which the only solution is $\phi = \frac{1}{2}\pi$, i.e. a circle. There *is* a spiral which is its own evolute, for which ϕ is the root of

$$\exp(\tfrac{3}{2}\pi \cot \phi) = \tan \phi,$$

or approximately $74° \, 39'$, only slightly different from the one under consideration. One might hazard the guess that this is the real property responsible for any supposed aesthetic excellence of a spiral of about this angle: that the tangent, along which the eye tends to travel, strikes the next coil of the spiral normally and gives a feeling of balance to the whole.

2.12. Some Miscellaneous Curves and Figures

We conclude this chapter with a list of curves and geometrical configurations which are suitable for inclusion in a permanent collection or for exhibition on public occasions.

2.12.1. Algebraic curves.

Many of these can be plotted point by point by solving quadratic equations only, on substituting $y = px$, or $y^2 = z$.

Of course, more advanced methods will usually give a rough picture of the curve more quickly.

Famous or interesting cubics — *For plotting substitute*

(1)	$x^3 + y^3 = 3axy$	folium of Descartes	$y = px$
(2)	$y = a^3/(x^2 + a^2)$	witch of Agnesi	values for x
(3)	$xy = x^3 - a^3$	trident	values for x
(4)	$x(x^2 + y^2) = ay^2$	cissoid	values for x
(5)	$y^2(a-x) = x^2(x+a)$	strophoid	values for x
(6)	$y^3 = x^2 - x^3$		values for x

Interesting quartics

(7)	$x^2 y^2 = x^2 + y^2$	'policeman on point-duty'	values for x
(8)	$x^4 = x^2 - y^2$	lemniscate	values for x
(9)	$xy(x^2 - y^2) = x^2 + y^2$	Maltese cross	$y = px$
(10)	$y^4 - x^4 = xy$	swastika	$y = px$
(11)	$y^2(y^2 - 96) = x^2(x^2 - 100)$	electric motor	$y^2 = z$
(12)	$12x^2 = y^3(4-y)$	peg-top	values for y
(13)	$x^4 + y^4 = a^2 xy$		$y = px$

(14)	$(x^2+2ay-a^2)^2 = y^2(a^2-x^2)$	cocked hat	values for x
(15)	$(x^2-1)^2 = y^2(3+2y)$	knot	values for y
(16)	$x^4+y^4 = 2axy^2$	bifoliate	$y^2 = z$
(17)	$x^4+x^2y^2+y^4 = x(x^2+y^2)$	bean	$y^2 = z$
(18)	$x^4+x^2y^2+y^4 = x(x^2-y^2)$	trefoil	$y^2 = z$
(19)	$(x^2+y^2-3x)^2 = 4x^2(2-x)$	links	values for x
(20)	$(y^2-x^2)(x-1)(2x-3)$ $= 4(x^2+y^2-2x)^2$	ampersand	$y^2 = z$
(21)	$(x^2-a^2)(x-a)^2+(y^2-a^2)^2$ $= 0$	bicuspidal	values for x
(22)	$(x^2-1)^2$ $= y^2(y-1)(y-2)(y+5)$	stirrup	values for y
(23)	$x^4 = x^2y-y^3$	bow	$y = px$

Higher degree curves

(24)	$y^2 = x^4-x^6$	dumb-bell	values for x
(25)	$y^2 = x^2y+x^5$	keratoid cusp	values for x
(26)	$y^2 = x^4+x^5$		values for x
(27)	$x^2 = x^6+y^6$	butterfly	values for x
(28)	$x^5+y^5 = 2x^2-5xy+2y^2$		$y = px$

Families of curves

$$y^2 = x(x^2-3)+c \qquad \text{for values } -2, 0, 2, 4, 6 \text{ of } c.$$

Confocal conics

$$\frac{x^2}{a^2+\lambda}+\frac{y^2}{b^2+\lambda} = 1.$$

Repeating patterns obtained from algebraic curves by replacing x and y by trigonometric functions of x and y. For example, from the folium $x^3+y^3 = 3axy$, trace for different values of a

$$\sin^3 x+\sin^3 y = 3a \sin x \sin y,$$
$$\sin^3 x+\tan^3 y = 3a \sin x \tan y,$$
$$\tan^3 x+\tan^3 y = 3a \tan x \tan y.$$

(The patterns are given in Frost's *Curve Tracing*, plate xv, fig. 4, and plate xvi, figs. 1 and 2.)

2.12.2. Polar curves. These are conveniently drawn on polar graph paper. They are arranged in inverse pairs (1–14);

each pair can be conveniently drawn on one sheet; if $a = 10$ cm, paper on which the largest circle is 30 cm in diameter is suitable.

(1)	$r = a\cos\theta$	circle
(2)	$r = a\sec\theta$	straight line
(3)	$r^2 = a^2\cos 2\theta$	lemniscate of Bernoulli
(4)	$r^2 = a^2\sec 2\theta$	rectangular hyperbola
(5)	$r = \frac{1}{2}a(1+\cos\theta)$	cardioid
(6)	$r = \frac{1}{2}a/(1+\cos\theta)$	parabola
(7)	$r = a(1+\frac{1}{2}\cos\theta)$	limaçon without loop
(8)	$r = a/(1+\frac{1}{2}\cos\theta)$	ellipse, eccentricity $\frac{1}{2}$
(9)	$r = a(\frac{1}{2}+\cos\theta)$	limaçon with loop
(10)	$r = a/(\frac{1}{2}+\cos\theta)$	hyperbola, eccentricity 2
(11)	$r = a\theta°/100$	Archimedean spiral
(12)	$r = 100a/\theta°$	reciprocal spiral
(13)	$r^2 = a^2\theta°/100$	parabolic spiral
(14)	$r^2 = 100a^2/\theta°$	lituus .
(15)	$r = ae^{\theta\cot\alpha}$	equiangular spiral (say
		$r = $ antilog $\theta°/1000$)
(16)	$r = a\cos n\theta$	rose-curves (rhodoneae); n petals if
		n is odd, $2n$ petals if n is even

(17) The limaçon family $r = a+b\cos\theta$ with variable b

(18) The family $r^n = a^n\cos n\theta$ for

$n = -2$	rectangular hyperbola
-1	straight line
$-\frac{1}{2}$	parabola
$+\frac{1}{2}$	cardioid
1	circle
$\frac{3}{2}, \frac{3}{5}$, etc.	intersecting loops
2	lemniscate of Bernoulli

2.12.3. Bipolar loci. P is a variable point, R and S are fixed. $PR = r$, $PS = s$, $RS = 2c$.

(1)	$r = \lambda s$	circle of Apollonius
	$r = s$	right bisector of RS
(2)	$\lambda r \pm \mu s = k$	Cartesian ovals
	$r+s = 2a$	ellipse
	$r-s = 2a$	hyperbola
	$r-s = c\sqrt{2}$	rectangular hyperbola

(3) $rs = k^2$ Cassinian ovals

 $rs = c^2$ lemniscate of Bernoulli

(4) $\dfrac{\lambda}{r} + \dfrac{\mu}{s} = k$ equipotential lines for charges λ, μ at R, S

(5) $\cos P\widehat{R}S + \cos P\widehat{S}R = k$ lines of force for magnet with
poles at R, S.

To draw the Cartesian ovals, first draw the lines $\lambda x \pm \mu y = k$. The ovals are then obtained as the loci of intersections of circles with centres R and S, whose radii are the (x, y)-coordinates of points on these lines.

To draw the Cassinian ovals, draw a circle containing a chord of length $2k$. Possible radii r, s are segments of chords through the mid-point of this chord.

2.12.4. Graphs of functions:

(1) The standard error curve $y = e^{-kx^2}$.

(2) The sine curve, the curve of damped S.H.M.

$$y = e^{-kx} \sin px,$$

and curves showing 'beats',

$$y = \sin mx + \sin nx, \quad m \doteqdot n.$$

(3) $y = x^x$

 $y = (1+x)^{1/x}$

 $y = (1+1/x)^x$

 $y^x = x^y$ (This involves difficult analysis. Do not forget the point $(-2, -4)$. Are there others in this quadrant for $y \neq x$?)

(4) The series of approximations to $y = \sin x$ obtained from the Maclaurin expansion

$$y = x, \quad x - \tfrac{1}{6}x^3, \quad x - \tfrac{1}{6}x^3 + \tfrac{1}{120}x^5, \quad \text{etc.}$$

(5) The series of approximations to $y = \tfrac{1}{2}x$ obtained from the Fourier expansion $(-\pi \leqslant x \leqslant \pi)$

$$y = \sin x, \quad \sin x - \tfrac{1}{2}\sin 2x, \quad \sin x - \tfrac{1}{2}\sin 2x + \tfrac{1}{3}\sin 3x, \quad \text{etc.}$$

(6) The 'pathological' functions

$$y = \sin\frac{1}{x}, \qquad y = x\sin\frac{1}{x}, \qquad y = x^2\sin\frac{1}{x},$$

on a large scale for x, say for $2 \geqslant |x| \geqslant \dfrac{1}{6\pi}$.

2.12.5. Configurations of interest:

(1) Orthogonal families of coaxal circles.

(2) The orthocentric quadrangle, with its nine-point circle, and the sixteen incircles and ecircles of the four triangles, touching it.

(3) The complete quadrilateral, with the four circumcircles of the triangles meeting in the Wallace point, the line of orthocentres, the circle of circumcentres, and the two families of orthogonal coaxal circles.

(4) The complete quadrangle, the four nine-point circles, the four pedal circles, and the circumcircle of the diagonal triangle, with their common point.

(5) Some of the Pascal lines of a six-point on a conic, and the Brianchon points of six tangents to a conic.

III

POLYHEDRA

3.1. INTRODUCTION

THE most suitable, and in many ways the most attractive, subject for an experiment in the construction of mathematical models is a set of polyhedra. The various types of polyhedra have exercised a great fascination over the minds of mathematicians of all ages, among them some of the greatest names in mathematics. It has even been said that Euclid's great work, *The Elements*, was not intended so much to be a textbook of geometry in general as to be an introduction to the five regular solids known to the ancient world. It begins with the construction of the equilateral triangle and ends with the construction of the icosahedron.

These five solids, the so-called Platonic solids, form the first and simplest group of polyhedra. They have regular faces, all congruent, and their vertices are regular polyhedral angles; that is to say, all the face-angles at every vertex and all the dihedral angles are equal. This can be expressed in another way by saying that the 'vertex-figure' formed by the lines, lying in the faces which meet at a particular vertex, which join the mid-points of the edges meeting at that vertex, is a regular polygon (Fig. 66). These requirements are not all necessary for a definition of a regular solid, but they are all true of it. As our aim is descriptive rather than deductive, we shall not go further into this question here.

A slight extension of the idea of a regular polygon to the 'star-polygon', which has equal sides and angles, but is not convex, leads to the next group of four polyhedra, which are associated with the names of Kepler and Poinsot; their faces or vertex figures are star-polygons, actually in all cases pentagrams. The pentagram is shown in Fig. 67; it is formed either by joining alternate vertices of a regular pentagon or by producing the edges until they meet the edges which are not their immediate neighbours. In a similar way the four Kepler–Poinsot polyhedra can be formed from the regular dodecahedron and icosahedron, either by drawing new planes through chains of vertices, for example, *PQRST* in Fig. 66, or by producing non-adjacent faces until they intersect. The first process is called *faceting*, the second, which is rather easier to visualize, *stellating*.

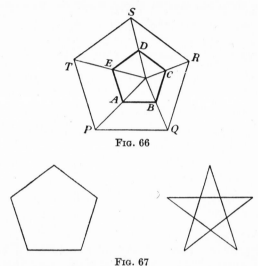

FIG. 66

FIG. 67

These four solids are also regular, and bring the total of regular solids up to nine.

The next class of solids comprises those which have some of the properties of the regular solids, but not all. If we forgo the requirement that the vertex figures shall be regular, and that the faces shall be all of one kind, but retain the conditions that the faces shall all be regular and that the vertex figures shall all be congruent, we obtain the set of *facially-regular*, or Archimedean solids, which contains two infinite groups, the prisms and antiprisms, and thirteen others. Correspondingly, if we interchange the conditions forgone and retained, we obtain the *vertically-regular* solids, or *Archimedean duals*, including the infinite families of dipyramids and trapezohedra, and thirteen others, among which are the rhombic dodecahedron and the rhombic triacontahedron.

There are also stellated Archimedean solids analogous to the Kepler–Poinsot solids in the regular case of which we shall give a few examples only.

Another interesting group of figures is the set of *regular compounds*, in which regular polyhedra having the same centre are combined to form solids of great symmetry and beauty.

From the point of view of construction the easiest polyhedra to make are those whose faces are all equilateral triangles. For these the name 'deltahedra' is proposed.

There are eight convex deltahedra, and an infinite number of non-convex ones, of which a few simpler examples are described.

The chapter concludes with examples of polyhedra which can be stacked together to fill space—solid tessellations—and a few miscellaneous models of interest.

3.2. DUALITY

A brief explanation must be given of this important principle as applied to polyhedra. In the cases in which we shall use it, it is equivalent to reciprocation with respect to a sphere. The *polar* of a point on a sphere with respect to that sphere is the tangent plane at the point; the point is the *pole* of the tangent plane. If the point is not on the sphere, but outside it, the polar plane passes through the points of contact of the tangents from the point. Conversely, the *pole* of a plane cutting a sphere is the point where the tangent planes at the points of section are concurrent. If a point lies inside a sphere, or the plane does not cut the sphere, their polar and pole can be obtained in real geometry from the reciprocal property that if P lies in the polar plane of Q, Q lies in the polar plane of P. Details will be familiar from the analogous two-dimensional case.

In three dimensions the line occupies an intermediate position. If two planes meet in a line l, their poles are joined by the *polar line* of l, and conversely. Thus a *duality* is established between points and planes, lines and lines. Every polyhedron can be *reciprocated* with respect to a sphere, each plane being replaced by its pole and each vertex by its polar plane, thereby constructing another, *dual* or *reciprocal,* polyhedron with the numbers of faces and vertices interchanged. It can be shown that, for a sphere, polar lines are perpendicular, and, for a suitable choice of radius, they can be made to intersect. This is the most interesting position in which reciprocal polyhedra can be placed, with each edge of one intersecting at right angles (and usually also at the mid-point) the corresponding edge of the other. Some of the regular compounds are formed in this way. We shall call this sphere, which touches all the edges of a polyhedron, the *intersphere,* and its radius the *inter-radius.*

3.3 MATERIALS AND CONSTRUCTION

3.3.1. Paper and cardboard. For complete beginners paper has the obvious advantage of cheapness, but it quickly gets dirty in use and is not easy to clean. In addition, a paper model is easily damaged and cannot be properly varnished or enamelled. Except for the very simplest polyhedra the folding of the nets without scoring is a difficult matter. Obviously, for any model which is to be at all permanent, cardboard will be used.

The card should be white with a good surface, and fairly thin, about the thickness of a plain postcard. Thick cardboard makes ugly corners, and allowance ought to be made for its thickness in drawing the net. It is useful, however, to cut flat sheets of thick card for internal strengthening in some of the stellated and interpenetrating polyhedra. Cartridge paper is not satisfactory unless it is stout enough to score half through without cutting, and for small models the manilla of thin filing folders or exercise-book covers is better. This does not need enamelling, and can be obtained in different colours. Interpenetrating solids can be made by adding manilla vertices of one colour to a polyhedron made of the other, for example, a model of the interlinked icosahedron and dodecahedron has been made in this way.

A knife or razor blade will be needed for cutting and scoring: preferably a Valet autostrop blade with a rigid back—wafer blades are dangerous and useless unless fixed in a special holder.

It should be used with a steel rule—set-squares and rulers of
wood or celluloid can quickly be cut to pieces!

3.3.2. Glass and 'Perspex'.

These have the great advantage that they are transparent, and therefore an inscribed model
can be clearly seen. Glass is awkward to cut accurately in polygonal
shapes and almost impossible to cement except at right
angles. 'Perspex' is easy to work and takes a high polish, but it
is expensive and scratches easily. A glass cube can be made out
of lantern-slide cover glasses ground and cemented at the edges,
open at the base, and standing on a wooden plinth. In this all
the Archimedean solids derived from the cube and octahedron
can be inscribed. For the solids derived from the dodecahedron
and icosahedron an icosahedron can be constructed out of 'Perspex',
made in two separate halves hinged together. The same
could be done with glass but it would be difficult to get the
edges of the equilateral triangles to adhere without using 'Sellotape'
(cellulose tape), or gumstrip.

As 'Perspex' is a comparatively new material, some hints on
handling it may not be out of place. Thin $\frac{1}{8}''$ or $\frac{3}{32}''$ sheet is the
best for models. The plasticized variety can be moulded after
heating in boiling water, but for polyhedra this is not necessary.
The figures to be cut can be scratched on it with a hard point.
It can be cut with a tenon-saw—a fine dovetail-saw is best—
which must be kept well oiled as the dust clogs the teeth. A
coping-saw can also be used, or best of all, a small hack-saw.
It can be planed in narrow thicknesses only, but it blunts the
tool, which must be kept very sharp and set very fine. It is also
possible to file it or grind it with carborundum. The edges can
easily be filed or planed down to any dihedral angle, which is a
great advantage in making polyhedra. Cementing is easy by
using the material itself dissolved in ethylene dichloride, carbon
tetrachloride, acetone, or xylene. The manufacturers also supply
a cement of this nature, 'Diakon No. 2'.

Great care must be taken to avoid scratching the material
while working it. It should be clamped and protected between
wood blocks as far as possible. Scratches which do occur can be
rubbed out with jeweller's rouge, or household scouring powder,

and the surface polished up with a metal polish or plate powder.

A heated compass point makes holes for thread or rivets, and the burr can be cut off with a knife. It is preferable, however, to use a drill.

3.3.3. Construction of cardboard models. The exterior perimeter of a net of a polyhedron which is all in one piece becomes a 'tree' of edges on the solid. This tree may be branched, but every edge is double and occurs twice on the perimeter of the net. It is evident that if these edges are numbered consecutively round the net every even edge will be joined to an odd edge in the final solid. This means that *tabs need only be attached to the even edges*. In the nets which follow, tabs are not shown unless there is special need to do so. In all other cases the rule is: *attach tabs to alternate edges round the net*.

There is an exception in the case of the last face, which is best left free of tabs. The missing tabs must be added to the other edges, and are best made large, so that a platform can be built up to which the last face can be stuck.

When the dimensions of the model have been decided on, the net can be constructed on the cardboard. In the case of a complicated net this is facilitated by pricking through vertices from a template drawn on tracing paper, but it must be done very accurately. Tabs are then added to alternate outside edges, care being taken to ensure that the angle at the shoulder of the tab is small enough to admit of the tab's being cemented to its appropriate face. The net can now be cut out with a razor-blade and the edges scored half-through for bending. (Where edges have to be scored on the back—in the stellated polyhedra—this is indicated in the diagrams.) The face of the net becomes the outside of the polyhedron.

For joining, a quick-drying cement, such as balsa-wood cement as used for model aircraft, is essential. After the cement has been applied to a tab, the edges to be joined are brought together, and the tab can be held down with a small wire paper-fastener while the cement dries. This is particularly useful in small models when the fingers cannot easily get inside, and near the finish of any model when there are several edges to be joined at once. A thin wire probe is sometimes useful in getting the last face to adhere.

If it is desired to make a set of polyhedra with the same inter-radius, or to be inscribed in a 'Perspex' cube or icosahedron, the dimensions can be calculated from the data given for each solid. It is important to remember that although the net is the outside of the polyhedron, its measurements give the *inside* measurements of the finished solid, because of the way the scored creases open at the fold. Allowance must therefore be made for the thickness of the card in calculating the necessary length of edge.

3.4. COLOURING POLYHEDRA

The attraction of a set of solid models is greatly increased if they are suitably coloured. A good enamel is best; coloured

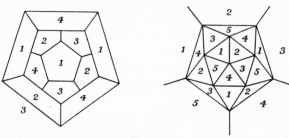

FIG. 68

dope is also suitable for the purpose. The Archimedean solids can be coloured so that all faces lying in planes of a circum-scribed cube are of one colour, those on the planes of a cir-cumscribed octahedron another, and similarly with the dodeca-hedron and icosahedron. The other planes in the rhombic polyhedra and the snubs require a third colour.

The dodecahedron itself exhibits the simplest 'regular' map requiring four colours, which can be allocated to its faces in two distinct ways.† The icosahedron requires only three colours; if five are used, the five faces at every vertex can be coloured

† See Rouse Ball, *Mathematical Recreations and Essays,* 11th edition, pp. 227 ff. A 'regular' map is one in which there are never more than three edges meeting at a vertex.

differently but opposite faces cannot then be coloured alike. This scheme is valuable for the great icosahedron.

The stellated polyhedra can be coloured to correspond with their regular relatives, and this helps greatly to make their planes and structure readily appreciable. The interpenetrating compounds demand of course that the individual solids composing them should have all faces of each coloured alike, while each is differently coloured from its companions. The schemes for the dodecahedron and icosahedron are shown in Fig. 68 on 'distorted representations'.

3.5. The Five Regular Platonic Polyhedra

In the following pages, which form a sort of 'atlas' of polyhedra, there is given for each solid

(1) its name and a symbol (to be explained);

(2) a perspective drawing of the solid;

(3) its 'net', i.e. the figure produced if the solid were made of cardboard, cut along a chain of edges, and opened out flat;

(4) the ratios of its edge to the radius of the intersphere, and to the edges of regular polyhedra in which it can be inscribed;

(5) the dihedral angles between its faces;

(6) one or more plans, or orthogonal projections of the solid; and

(7) a table of the number of faces, vertices, and edges.

Fuller details are given in Table II. The symbol used to indicate the polyhedra is a modification of that invented by Schläfli. He gave the number of sides in the (regular) face and in the (regular) vertex figure; thus the cube is $\{4, 3\}$. This does not extend to the Archimedean solids, so that we prefer here to write (as an index) the number of faces of each kind at each vertex (cf. 2.9.2). The cube is therefore written 4^3, and a snub cube $3^4.4$.

Since each side of a regular polygon of p sides subtends an angle of $2\pi/p$ at the centre, whereas the side of a pentagram subtends $4\pi/5$, it is convenient to call the pentagram $\{5/2\}$, and generally to denote by {p} a polygon whose sides subtend $2\pi/p$ at its centre ($p > 2$). This is a regular convex polygon of p sides if p is integral, and a stellated polygon of n sides, enclosing the centre d times, if p is a fraction n/d in its lowest terms.

For the Archimedean duals, the vertex figures are now regular, and of different kinds, while the faces are not. This is denoted by prefixing V to the symbol, which now refers to the number and arrangement of vertex figures round each face. Thus the rhombic-dodecahedron, the dual of the cuboctahedron 3.4.3.4 or $(3.4)^2$, is $V(3.4)^2$.

The tetrahedron, cube, and octahedron occur naturally in the form of certain crystals; the skeletons of the radiolarians *Circoporus octahedrus, Circogonia icosahedra, Circorrhegma dodecahedra* have the form implied by their name (D'Arcy Thompson, *On Growth and Form*, p. 726, fig. 340).

3.5.1. Tetrahedron. 3^3

Net:

Fig. 69

Fig. 70

$$\frac{\text{Edge}}{\text{Inter-radius}} = 2\sqrt{2} = 2\cdot828.$$

Dihedral angle $= 70° 32'$.

Plans:

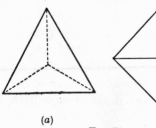

(a)

(b)

Fig. 71

F	V	E
4	4	6

Self-dual.

3.5.2. Cube. 4^3

NET:

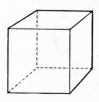 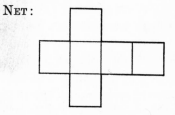

FIG. 72   FIG. 73

$$\frac{\text{Edge}}{\text{Inter-radius}} = \sqrt{2} = 1\cdot414.$$

Dihedral angle $= 90°$.

PLAN:

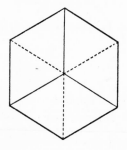

FIG. 74

F	V	E
6	8	12

Dual of octahedron.

3.5.3. Octahedron. 3^4

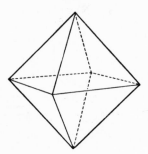

Fig. 75

Net:

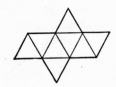

Fig. 76

$$\frac{\text{Edge}}{\text{Inter-radius}} = 2.$$

Dihedral angle $= 109° 28'$.

Plan:

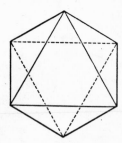

Fig. 77

F	V	E
8	6	12

Dual of cube.

3.5.4. Dodecahedron. 5^3

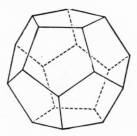

Fig. 78

Net:

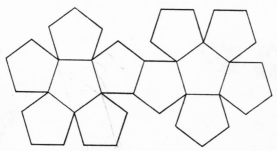

Fig. 79

$$\frac{\text{Edge}}{\text{Inter-radius}} = 3 - \sqrt5 = 0.7639.$$

Dihedral angle $= 116° 34' (= \pi - \tan^{-1}2)$.

$26°34'$

Plan:

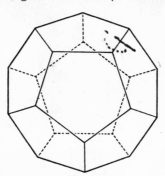

Fig. 80

F	V	E
12	20	30

Dual of icosahedron.

3.5.5. Icosahedron. 3^5

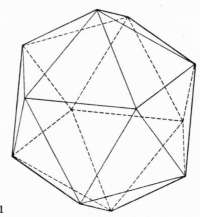

FIG. 81

NET:

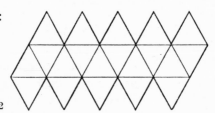

FIG. 82

$$\frac{\text{Edge}}{\text{Inter-radius}} = \sqrt{5}-1 = 1\cdot236.$$

Dihedral angle $= 138° \; 11' \; (\pi-\sin^{-1}\tfrac{2}{3}).$

PLAN:

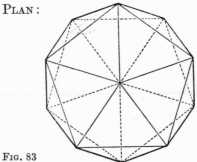

FIG. 83

F	V	E	
20	12	30	Dual of dodecahedron.

3.6. The Kepler–Poinsot Polyhedra

These four beautiful solids were unknown to the ancient world and were not discovered until modern times. The two with star faces—the two stellated dodecahedra—were found by Kepler (1571–1630); the others with regular faces and star vertices—the great icosahedron and dodecahedron—by Poinsot (1777–1859). They are technically speaking regular polyhedra, and with the five Platonic solids bring the total number of regular polyhedra up to nine, which are all shown in Plate 1 a. It can be proved that this exhausts the possibilities, apart from compounds. On account of their re-entrant angles, their construction is more difficult than that of ordinary convex polyhedra, and care must be taken to ensure adequate rigidity. The solids are not deformable in theory, but in practice slight gaps at the corners and other inaccuracies lead to considerable distortion unless due precautions are taken. Means of doing this are suggested for the individual solids.

They are peculiarly pleasing if suitably coloured and the planes of the faces can be clearly seen. One has the satisfaction of having constructed a polyhedron whose very existence was denied by at least one mathematician. (The small stellated and great dodecahedra do not satisfy Euler's theorem

$$F+V = E+2$$

in its usual form. For this reason it was supposed by Schläfli that they could not exist.)

3.6.1. Small stellated dodecahedron. $(\frac{5}{2})^5$

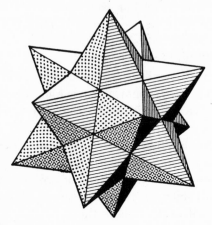

FIG. 84

F	V	E
12	12	30

Dual of great dodecahedron.

PLAN:

FIG. 85

Construction of net. Each pentahedral pyramid can be formed from half of a plane decagon as shown (Fig. 86 *a* and *b*); twelve of these fitted together form the complete net. One way of fitting the vertices together is given below.

Construction of solid. It is advisable not to use the complete net, but to build the solid up from pentahedral pyramids

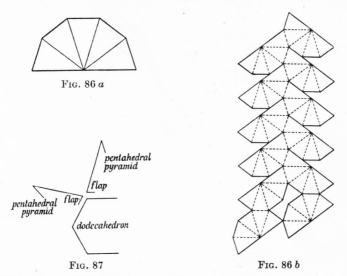

Fig. 86 *a*

pentahedral pyramid

flap

pentahedral pyramid *flap*

dodecahedron

Fig. 87   Fig. 86 *b*

attached to an inscribed dodecahedron, and cement edge to edge. The edges that coincide with a dodecahedral edge must be provided *each* with a flap instead of alternately; these flaps can then be fastened to the dodecahedral faces (Fig. 87).

$$\frac{\text{Edge}}{\text{Edge of inscribed dodecahedron}} = 2 + \sqrt{5} = 4\cdot236.$$

$$\frac{\text{Edge}}{\text{Inter-radius}} = \sqrt{5} + 1 = 3\cdot236.$$

Dihedral angle $= 116° \; 34'$.

(Re-entrant angle $= 116° \; 34'$.)

Comparing Fig. 67 with Fig. 63, it is evident that the sides of a pentagram are divided by the 'false vertices' in the ratio $\tau : 1 : \tau$.

3.6.2. The great dodecahedron. $5^{\frac{5}{2}}$

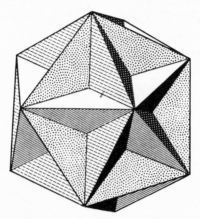

FIG. 88

$$\frac{\text{Edge}}{\text{Edge of inscribed dodecahedron}} = \frac{3+\sqrt5}{2} = 2\cdot618.$$

$$\frac{\text{Edge}}{\text{Inter-radius}} = \sqrt5-1 = 1\cdot236.$$

Dihedral angle $= 63° \ 26'.$

(Re-entrant angle $= 116° \ 34'.$)

PLAN:

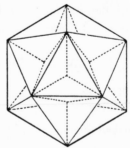

FIG. 89

F	V	E
12	12	30

Dual of small stellated dodecahedron.

Construction of net. Since the face angles at each true star-pointed vertex add up to 360° (36° × 10), the net is particularly simple; one form of it is given below. All solid lines

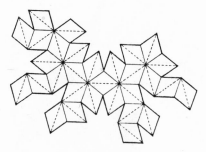

are to be cut or scored on one side; the dotted lines are scored on the other side.

Construction of solid. This net usually makes a rigid model without any additional strengthening, but the vertices where ten cuts meet tend to break. They can be covered with small paper circles, since the sum of the face angles at each vertex is 360°.

Alternatively, three of the twelve pentagons can be made solid, for example, those attached to the edges of one of the triangles. The indented trihedron can then be made to fit in this triangle; three five-pointed stars and a unit for four more indented trihedra complete the solid.

3.6.3. Great stellated dodecahedron. $(\frac{5}{2})^3$

Fig. 91

F	V	E
12	20	30

Dual of great icosahedron.

Plan:

Fig. 92

Construction of net. The solid consists of twenty triangular pyramids circumscribing an icosahedron, one on each face.

The net of a single pyramid is easily constructed as follows:

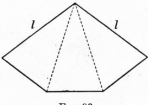

FIG. 93

Construction of solid. The easiest way to build the solid is to make the pyramids hinged in pairs and to cement them to an icosahedron by means of base flaps as shown.

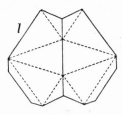

FIG. 94

$$\frac{\text{Edge}}{\text{Edge of inscribed icosahedron}} = 4 \cdot 236.$$

$$\frac{\text{Edge}}{\text{Inter-radius}} = 3 + \sqrt{5} = 5 \cdot 236.$$

$$\frac{l}{\text{Edge}} = \frac{3 - \sqrt{5}}{2} = 0 \cdot 382. \qquad \frac{l}{\text{Inter-radius}} = 2.$$

Dihedral angle $= 63° \; 26'$.

3.6.4. The great icosahedron. $3^{\frac{5}{2}}$

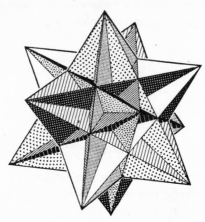

Fig. 95

$$\frac{\text{Edge}}{\text{Edge of inscribed icosahedron}} = \frac{7+3\sqrt{5}}{2} = 6{\cdot}854.$$

$$\frac{\text{Edge}}{\text{Inter-radius}} = \sqrt{5}+1 = 3{\cdot}236.$$

Dihedral angle $= 41° \ 49'$.   (Re-entrant angles $= 109° \ 28'$.)

$$\frac{l}{\text{Inter-radius}} = \sqrt{5}-1 = 1{\cdot}236. \qquad \frac{m}{l} = \frac{\sqrt{5}-1}{2} = 0{\cdot}618.$$

PLAN:

Fig. 96

F	V	E
20	12	30

Dual of great stellated
dodecahedron $(\frac{5}{2})^3$.

Construction of net. The figure shows the eighteen lines in which a face of the icosahedron is cut by eighteen other faces (excluding the face itself and the parallel plane). The sides of

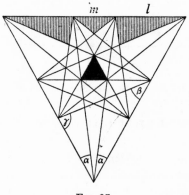

Fig. 97

the triangle are divided in golden section $\tau:1:\tau$. The inner solid triangle is the face of the inscribed icosahedron. The shaded portions are elements of the net which come together (from three different planes) at a concave false vertex; from them the net can be constructed. The three fit together as follows:

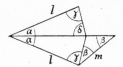

Fig. 98

$$\alpha = 22° \, 14'; \;\; \beta+\gamma = 120°; \;\; \beta = 37° \, 46' = 60°-\alpha; \;\; \gamma = 82° \, 14' = 60°+\alpha;$$
$$\delta = 75° \, 32'.$$

Five of these pieces fit together at each vertex of the solid; the whole solid is made of sixty of them.

The arrangement at a vertex is shown on p. 98 (Fig. 99).

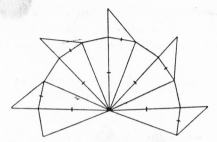

Fig. 99. NET OF A SINGLE VERTEX. [Marked lines must be scored on the *back*.
Note that the marked radii are *longer* than their neighbours.]

Construction of great icosahedron.
This polyhedron is theoretically rigid, but in practice it will usually be found slightly deformable. Furthermore when so many edges, scored alternately front and back, meet at each vertex, there is a tendency for the card to break away, notably at the re-entrant (false) vertices where there are many joins. It is advisable therefore to construct the model in a different way.

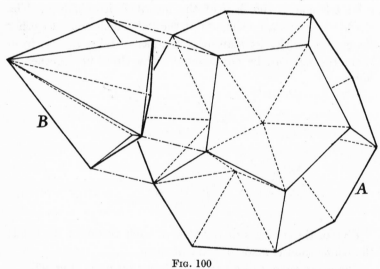

Fig. 100

We begin by making the solid 'A' (Fig. 100) which is a dodeca-hedron with pentagonal dimples, all of whose faces are equilateral triangles. This is in fact a deltahedron (see 3.11), and its net is given below (Fig. 101). Now make twelve vertices 'B' using the

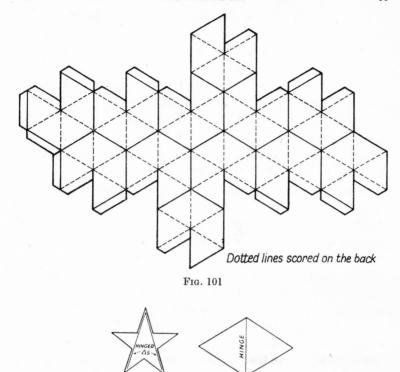

Dotted lines scored on the back

Fig. 101

HINGED
Δs

HINGE

Fig. 102

net given in Fig. 99. It is best to strengthen each internally with two hinged equilateral triangles, as indicated in Fig. 102, inserted into the star-polyhedral angles from inside. The twelve 'B's are now cemented into the twelve dimples in 'A', and the solid is complete. This method was communicated to us by Mr. N. J. Bridge and is used by permission.

3.7. The Archimedean Polyhedra

The Archimedean, or semi-regular polyhedra, are what is called 'facially' regular. This means that every face is a regular polygon, though the faces are not all of the same kind. Every vertex, however, is to be congruent to every other vertex, i.e. the faces must be arranged in the same order around each vertex.

The regular prisms, which consist of two congruent regular polygons similarly placed in parallel planes, with corresponding vertices joined by edges, satisfy the definition of facially regular solids if the side faces are squares. The definition is also satisfied by the series of regular prismoids or antiprisms. In these there are also two parallel plane faces which are congruent regular polygons, but one polygon is twisted so that each of its vertices is midway between two vertices of the other, to each of which it is joined. The side faces are thus triangles, and if they are equilateral the prismoid is facially regular.

There is no limit to the number of members in each of these series, and they are not of particular interest. It can be proved (see, for example, Lines's *Solid Geometry*) that apart from these there are only thirteen Archimedean solids, two of which occur in two forms. These two are the two 'snubs', and the two forms of each are related to one another like a left-hand and a right-hand glove: they are *enantiomorphic*. The set of thirteen is illustrated in Plate 2 *a*.

One of these solids, the truncated tetrahedron, can be inscribed in a regular tetrahedron. The next six can be inscribed in either a cube or an octahedron, and the last six in either a dodecahedron or an icosahedron. The 'truncated' solids are so called because each can be constructed by cutting off the corners of some other solid, but the truncated cuboctahedron and icosidodecahedron require a distortion in addition to convert rectangles into squares. So the better names for these two solids are 'Great Rhombicuboctahedron' and 'Great Rhombicosidodecahedron'. The solids 3.4^3 and $3.4.5.4$ can then bear the prefix 'small'. The syllable 'rhomb-' shows that one set of faces lies in the planes of the rhombic dodecahedron and rhombic triacontahedron respectively. All Archimedean solids are inscribable in a sphere.

3.7.1. Truncated tetrahedron. 3.6^2

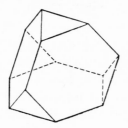

FIG. 103

NET:

FIG. 104

$$\frac{\text{Edge}}{\text{Tetrahedral edge}} = \frac{1}{3}. \qquad \frac{\text{Edge}}{\text{Inter-radius}} = \frac{\sqrt{8}}{3} = 0\cdot943.$$

Dihedral angles: 70° 32′, 109° 28′.

PLAN:

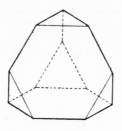

FIG. 105

F_3	F_6	V	E
4	4	12	18

3.7.2. Cuboctahedron. $(3.4)^2$

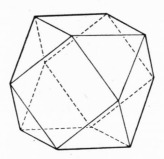

Fig. 106

NET:

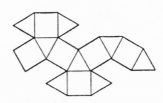

Fig. 107

$$\frac{\text{Edge}}{\text{Cube edge}} = \frac{1}{\sqrt{2}} = 0{\cdot}707. \qquad \frac{\text{Edge}}{\text{Octahedral edge}} = \frac{1}{2}.$$

$$\frac{\text{Edge}}{\text{Inter-radius}} = \frac{2}{\sqrt{3}}.$$

Dihedral angle $= 125° \, 16'$.

PLAN:

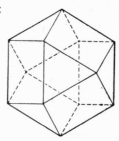

Fig. 108

F_3	F_4	V	E	
8	6	12	24	Dual of rhombic dodecahedron.

3.7.3. Truncated cube. 3.8^2

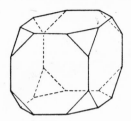

FIG. 109

NET:

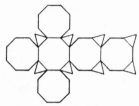

FIG. 110

$$\frac{\text{Edge}}{\text{Cube edge}} = \sqrt{2}-1 = 0.414.$$

$$\frac{\text{Edge}}{\text{Octahedral edge}} = 3\sqrt{2}-4 = 0.243.$$

$$\frac{\text{Edge}}{\text{Inter-radius}} = 2-\sqrt{2} = 0.586.$$

Dihedral angles: $90°$, $125° 16'$.

PLAN:

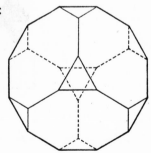

FIG. 111

F_3	F_8	V	E
8	6	24	36

3.7.4. Truncated octahedron. 4.6^2

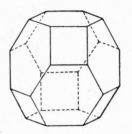

FIG. 112

NET:

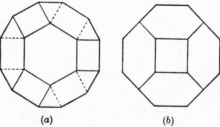

FIG. 113

$$\frac{\text{Edge}}{\text{Octahedral edge}} = \frac{1}{3}. \qquad \frac{\text{Edge}}{\text{Cube edge}} = \frac{1}{2\sqrt{2}} = 0{\cdot}354.$$

$$\frac{\text{Edge}}{\text{Inter-radius}} = \frac{2}{3}.$$

Dihedral angles: $125° \ 16'$, $109° \ 28'$.

PLANS:

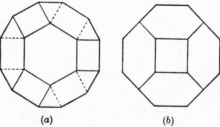

(a)   (b)

FIG. 114

F_4	F_6	V	E
6	8	24	36

3.7.5. (Small) rhombicuboctahedron. 3.4^3

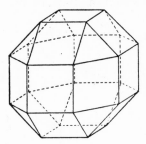

Fɪɢ. 115

Nᴇᴛ:

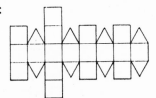

Fɪɢ. 116

$$\frac{\text{Edge}}{\text{Cube edge}} = \sqrt{2} - 1 = 0\cdot414.$$

$$\frac{\text{Edge}}{\text{Octahedral edge}} = \frac{\sqrt{2}}{3+\sqrt{2}} = 0\cdot320.$$

$$\frac{\text{Edge}}{\text{Inter-radius}} = (2-\sqrt{2})^{\frac{1}{2}} = 0\cdot7654.$$

Dihedral angles: $135°$, $144° \, 44'$.

Pʟᴀɴs:

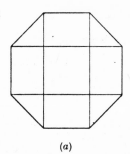

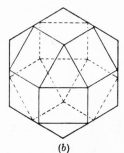

Fɪɢ. 117

(a)   (b)

F_3	F_4	V	E
8	18	24	48

3.7.6. Great rhombicuboctahedron or truncated cuboctahedron. 4.6.8

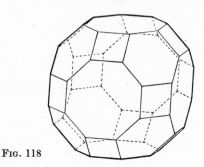

FIG. 118

NET:

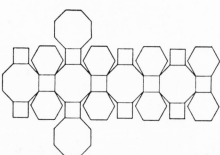

FIG. 119

$$\frac{\text{Edge}}{\text{Cube edge}} = \frac{2\sqrt{2}-1}{7} = 0\cdot261.$$

$$\frac{\text{Edge}}{\text{Octahedral edge}} = \frac{2-\sqrt{2}}{3} = 0\cdot195.$$

$$\frac{\text{Edge}}{\text{Inter-radius}} = \left(\frac{2-\sqrt{2}}{3}\right)^{\frac{1}{2}} = 0\cdot4419.$$

Dihedral angles: $135°$ $(8\text{--}4)$, $125°$ $16'$ $(8\text{--}6)$, $144°$ $44'$ $(6\text{--}4)$.

PLANS:

FIG. 120 (a)

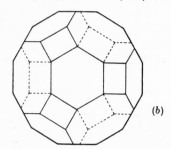

(b)

F_4	F_6	F_8	V	E
12	8	6	48	72

3.7.7. Snub cube. $3^4.4$

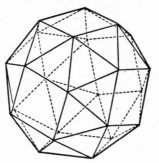

FIG. 121 (*dextro*)

NET:

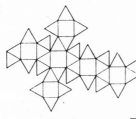
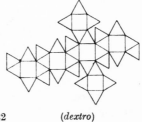

(*laevo*)   FIG. 122   (*dextro*)

$$\frac{\text{Edge}}{\text{Cube edge}} = 0 \cdot 438 \ (\tfrac{7}{16} \text{ very approximately}).$$

$$\frac{\text{Edge}}{\text{Octahedral edge}} = 0 \cdot 336.$$

$$\frac{\text{Edge}}{\text{Inter-radius}} = 0 \cdot 8018.$$

Dihedral angles: $142° \ 59'$ (4–3), $153° \ 14'$ (3–3).

PLAN:

FIG. 123

F_3	F_4	V	E
32	6	24	60

3.7.8. Icosidodecahedron. $(3.5)^2$

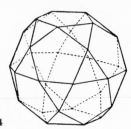

FIG. 124

NET:

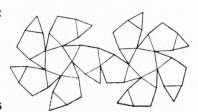

FIG. 125

$$\frac{\text{Edge}}{\text{Dodecahedral edge}} = \sin 54° = \frac{\sqrt{5}+1}{4} = 0\text{·}809.$$

$$\frac{\text{Edge}}{\text{Icosahedral edge}} = \frac{1}{2}.$$

$$\frac{\text{Edge}}{\text{Inter-radius}} = 2\tan 18° = 0\text{·}6498.$$

Dihedral angle: 142° 37′.

PLAN:

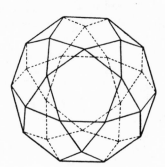

FIG. 126

F_3	F_5	V	E
20	12	30	60

Dual of rhombic triacontahedron.

3.7.9. Truncated dodecahedron. 3.10^2

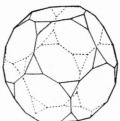

FIG. 127

NET:

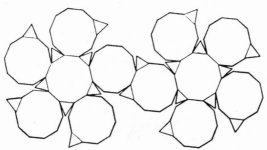

FIG. 128

$$\frac{\text{Edge}}{\text{Dodecahedral edge}} = \frac{1}{\sqrt{5}} = 0 \cdot 447.$$

$$\frac{\text{Edge}}{\text{Icosahedral edge}} = \frac{3\sqrt{5}-1}{22} = 0 \cdot 259.$$

$$\frac{\text{Edge}}{\text{Inter-radius}} = \frac{3}{\sqrt{5}} - 1 = 0 \cdot 3416.$$

Dihedral angles: $116° \ 34'$ (10–10), $142° \ 37'$ (10–3).

PLAN:

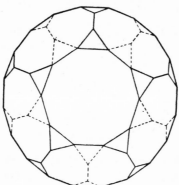

FIG. 129

F_3	F_{10}	V	E
20	12	60	90

3.7.10. Truncated icosahedron. 5.6^2

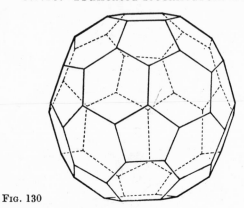

Fig. 130

NET:

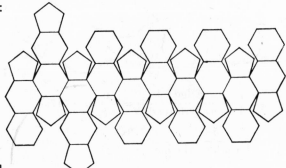

Fig. 131

$$\frac{\text{Edge}}{\text{Icosahedral edge}} = \frac{1}{3}. \qquad \frac{\text{Edge}}{\text{Dodecahedral edge}} = \frac{7+5\sqrt{5}}{38} = 0.478.$$

Dihedral angles: $138°\ 11'$ (6–6), $142°\ 37'$ (6–5).

PLAN:

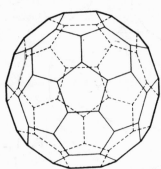

$$\frac{\text{Edge}}{\text{Inter-radius}} = \frac{\sqrt{5}-1}{3}$$
$$= 0.4120.$$

Fig. 132

F_5	F_6	V	E
12	20	60	90

3.7.11. (Small) rhombicosidodecahedron. 3.4.5.4

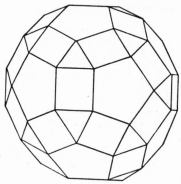

Fig. 133

Net:

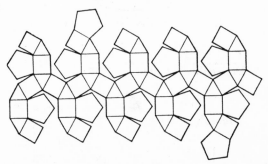

Fig. 134

$$\frac{\text{Edge}}{\text{Dodecahedral edge}} = \frac{\sqrt{5}+1}{6} = 0\cdot539.$$

$$\frac{\text{Edge}}{\text{Icosahedral edge}} = \frac{3\sqrt{5}+1}{22} = 0\cdot350.$$

Dihedral angles: 148° 17′ (5–4), 159° 6′ (3–4).

$$\frac{\text{Edge}}{\text{Inter-radius}} = \sqrt{2}\tan 18°$$

$$= 0\cdot4595.$$

Plan:

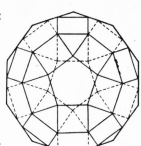

F_3	F_4	F_5	V	E
20	30	12	60	120

Fig. 135

3.7.12. Great rhombicosidodecahedron or truncated icosidodecahedron. 4.6.10

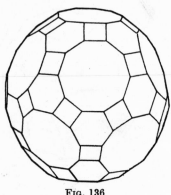

FIG. 136

$$\frac{\text{Edge}}{\text{Dodecahedral edge}} = \frac{\sqrt{5}+1}{10} = 0.324.$$

$$\frac{\text{Edge}}{\text{Icosahedral edge}} = \frac{\sqrt{5}-1}{6} = 0.206.$$

$$\frac{\text{Edge}}{\text{Inter-radius}} = \sqrt{\tfrac{2}{3}}\,\tan 18° = 0.2653.$$

Dihedral angles: 148° 17′ (10–4), 142° 37′ (10–6), 159° 6′ (6–4).

3.7.12. Great rhombicosidodecahedron (*cont.*)

NET:

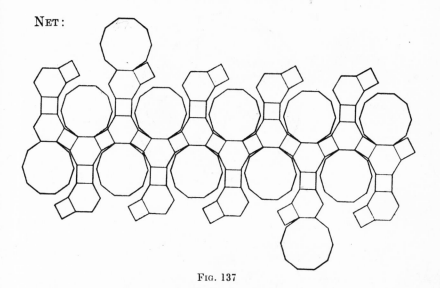

FIG. 137

PLAN:

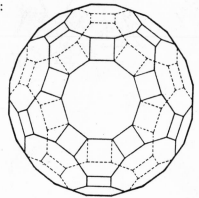

FIG. 138

F_4	F_6	F_{10}	V	E
30	20	12	120	180

3.7.13. Snub dodecahedron. $3^4.5$

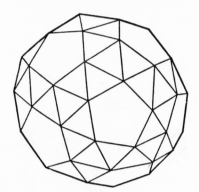

FIG. 139 (*dextro*

NET:

FIG. 140 (*dextro*)

$$\frac{\text{Edge}}{\text{Dodecahedral edge}} = 0.562.$$

$$\frac{\text{Edge}}{\text{Icosahedral edge}} = 0.364.$$

$$\frac{\text{Edge}}{\text{Inter-radius}} = 0.4769.$$

Dihedral angles: 152° 56′ (5–3), 164° 11′ (3–3).

3.7.13. Snub dodecahedron (*cont.*)

PLAN:

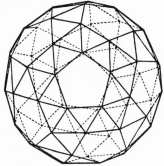

FIG. 141

$$F_3 \quad F_5 \quad V \quad E$$
$$80 \quad 12 \quad 60 \quad 150$$

3.7.14. Isomerism. In the course of construction of Archimedean polyhedra, it will be discovered that several of them can be 'wrongly' assembled. This means that two or more polyhedra exist with the same specifications in terms of the number of faces of each type, but with these faces differently arranged. This is a phenomenon rather like that of isomerism in chemistry, where several different molecules may exist with the same number of atoms of each kind, but differently arranged. Isomeric forms among the Archimedeans are as follows.

(*a*) The cuboctahedron $(3.4)^2$. If this is made in two halves, one half can be given a sixth of a turn relative to the other before assembly.

(*b*) The rhombicuboctahedron 3.4^3 can be altered by giving one of its octagonal caps an eighth of a turn. In this case, although the symmetry of the solid is reduced, the local character of the vertices is not changed.

(*c*) The icosidodecahedron $(3.5)^2$ can be altered similarly by rotating one half through 36° relative to the other.

(*d*) The rhombicosidodecahedron $3.4.5.4$ admits a variety of isomeric forms. It has decagonal caps, up to three of which can be similarly rotated through 36°.

3.8. DUAL SOLIDS

By the Principle of Duality, every three-dimensional figure composed of points, lines, and planes has a figure dual to it whose planes correspond to the points of the original figure and vice versa. In the case of the regular and Archimedean polyhedra, which are all inscribable in a sphere, the simplest way to produce such a dual solid is to replace every vertex by the tangent plane to this sphere, thereby obtaining a polyhedron with analogous 'regular' features. It is easily seen that the dual of a regular polyhedron formed in this way is itself regular; that of an Archimedean facially-regular solid is what is called 'vertically-regular', i.e. it has all its faces congruent and all its polyhedral angles regular (though of course not all identical). There is thus a vertically-regular solid corresponding to every Archimedean polyhedron.

These solids are of considerable importance in the study of crystals, as a number of them are themselves crystal forms, or are 'regularized' versions of the crystal form. They are perhaps less attractive than the Archimedean solids, no doubt because the eye does not readily appreciate the regularity of the vertical angles, and is impressed only by the irregularity of the faces. Also their symmetry is less easily demonstrated by painting the faces in different colours.

Two of these solids are here fully depicted, namely those with rhombic faces. These are the duals of the cuboctahedron and the icosidodecahedron and have twelve and thirty faces respectively. They are accordingly known as the rhombic dodecahedron and the rhombic triacontahedron. The diagonals of their faces are the edges of the cube and octahedron, the dodecahedron and icosahedron respectively. The corresponding 'rhombic' solid whose diagonals are two dually placed tetrahedra is the cube.

Note that a cube can be divided into six square pyramids by joining its vertices to its centre; if these are placed outwards on the faces of another cube, the rhombic dodecahedron results.

In the case of the remainder, a sketch of an element only of the net is given, and a photograph of a set of models is shown in Plate 2b. Full data of all the Archimedean solids (except prisms and antiprisms) and their duals are given in Table II, and from this the reader can construct the full nets and the solids without difficulty.

The duals of the prisms and antiprisms are the Archimedean dipyramids and trapezohedra. The dipyramid can be thought of as two 'regular' pyramids placed base to base, having a central regular polygon of edges, and two additional polyhedral vertices on opposite sides of it. If the four dihedral angles at a vertex on the central polygon are equal, the dipyramid is Archimedean. The trapezohedron has a central zigzag of edges, and two additional polyhedral vertices. The edges arising from one of these vertices meet the central zigzag alternately with the edges arising from the other vertex, so that three edges meet at each central vertex. If the three dihedral angles so formed are equal, the trapezohedron is Archimedean. The faces are all 'kites', i.e. quadrilaterals with two pairs of adjacent equal sides.

The face of any dual solid can be constructed by taking the vertex-figure of the original Archimedean solid (see p. 76). This figure has a circumscribing circle, which is now drawn. If the tangents to this circle are drawn at each vertex of the vertex-figure, they will form the face of the dual solid. (This method of construction is due to Mr. Dorman Luke.)

Note that while the Archimedean solids have a circumscribed sphere, their duals have an inscribed sphere. All alike have an intersphere touching their edges. Data giving the ratios of the radii of these various spheres for all the polyhedra here considered are given in Table II.

TABLE I

Nets of Archimedean Duals

Name	Symbol	Element of net	Number of elements	Net similar to that of:
Triakis Tetrahedron	V.3.6^2		4	Tetrahedron
Triakis Octahedron	V.3.8^2		8	Octahedron
Tetrakis Hexahedron	V.4.6^2		6	Cube
Trapezoidal Icositetrahedron	V.3.4^3		8	Octahedron in two sets of four
Hexakis Octahedron	V.4.6.8		8	Octahedron in two sets of four
Pentagonal Icositetrahedron (snub, two en-antiomorphs)	V.3^4.4		8	Octahedron in two sets of four

TABLE I (cont.)

Name	Symbol	Element of net	Number of elements	Net similar to that of:
Triakis Icosahedron	V.3.10^2		20	Icosahedron
Pentakis Dodecahedron	V.5.6^2		12	Dodecahedron
Trapezoidal Hexecontahedron	V.3.4.5.4		12	,,
Hexakis Icosahedron	V.4.6.10		12	,,
Pentagonal Hexecontahedron (snub, two enantiomorphs)	V.3^4.5		12	,,

3.8.1. Rhombic dodecahedron. $V(3.4)^2$

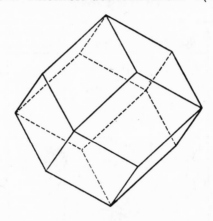

Fig. 142

(a) Net

(b) Single face

Fig. 143

$$\frac{\text{Edge}}{\text{Inter-radius}} = \frac{3\sqrt{2}}{4} = 1.0607.$$

Dihedral angle $= 120°$. Ratio of diagonals $= \sqrt{2}:1$.

PLANS:

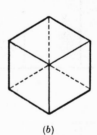

(a)   (b)

Fig. 144

F	V	E
12	14	24

3.8.2. Rhombic triacontahedron. $V(3.5)^2$

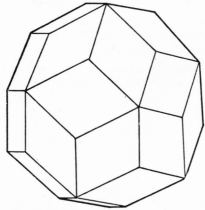

FIG. 145

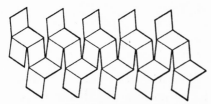

FIG. 146 (a). Net

FIG. 146 (b). Single face

$$\frac{\text{Edge}}{\text{Inter-radius}} = \frac{5-\sqrt{5}}{4} = 0\cdot6910.$$

Dihedral angle $= 144°$.

Ratio of diagonals $= (\sqrt{5}+1):2 = 1\cdot618:1.$

F	V	E
30	32	60

PLANS:

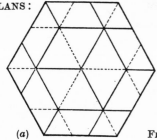

(a)

FIG. 147

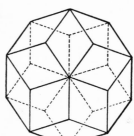

(b)

3.8.3. The rhombic dodecahedron and the cube.

If a cube is divided by the six diametral planes which pass through pairs of opposite edges, it breaks up into six square pyramids. If these pyramids are assembled outwards on the faces of another cube, the result is a rhombic dodecahedron. A model to show this is interesting. Make the six square pyramids of card from the net shown (Fig. 148). Before sticking up the bases, glue the

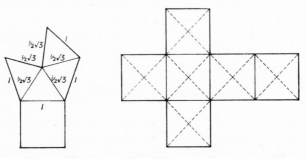

Fig. 148

bases to a stout tape (or, rather, two crossed tapes) in the form of a cube-net. The resulting chain of pyramids can be turned inwards to form a cube, or, turned outwards, placed as a jacket over another cube to form the rhombic dodecahedron.

3.8.4. The dodecahedron and the cube.

In a very similar way a 'roof' can be placed on each face of a cube to form a regular dodecahedron. The net for each 'roof' is given in Fig. 149. The complete solid appears in Fig. 166 (a).

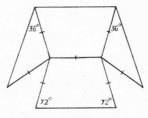

Fig. 149

3.9. Stellated Archimedean Polyhedra

Just as the class of regular solids can be extended to include the Kepler–Poinsot polyhedra, so the class of Archimedeans can be extended to include stellated Archimedean figures with star-faces or star-vertices, or both. This is a large class, and its size depends on the precise restrictions made. For example, some 'polyhedra' have planes which pass through the centre of symmetry, both sides of which appear on the 'outside' of the figure. One such will be found in the section on deltahedra.

Here we give plans of four members of the class; the reader who has successfully made the great icosahedron will be able to construct the nets for himself. They are the 'quasi-regular' great dodecadodecahedron and great icosidodecahedron (which bear the same relation to the Kepler–Poinsot solids as the cuboctahedron and icosidodecahedron to the Platonic) and their duals, the small and great stellated triacontahedra.

A full account of stellated Archimedean polyhedra can be found in 'Uniform polyhedra', by Coxeter, Longuet-Higgins, and Miller, *Phil. Trans.* A, **246** (1954), 401–50.

3.9.1. Great dodecadodecahedron. $(5 \cdot \frac{5}{2})^2$

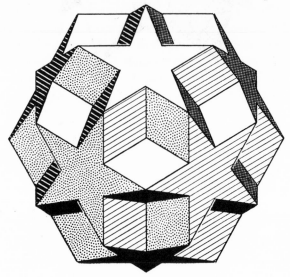

Fig. 150

3.9.2. Great icosidodecahedron. $(3.\tfrac{5}{2})^2$

Fig. 151

3.9.3. Small stellated triacontahedron. $V(5.\frac{5}{2})^2$

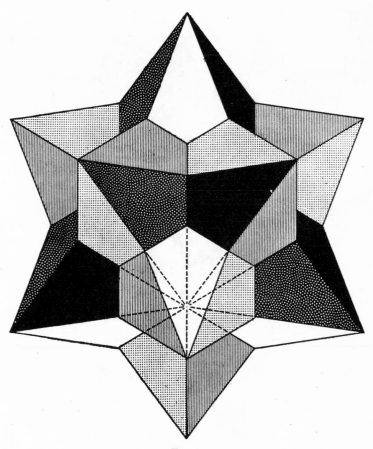

Fig. 152

3.9.4. Great stellated triacontahedron. $V(3.\frac{5}{2})^2$

FIG. 153

3.9.5. The stellated rhombic dodecahedron

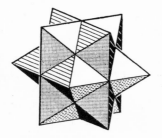

FIG. 154

One figure formed by stellating an Archimedean dual is of special interest—the stellated rhombic dodecahedron. This is a solid with the vertices of a cuboctahedron; each face consists of a pair of overlapping triangles. The solid is shown in Fig. 154.

An interlocking puzzle in the form of this solid used formerly to be on sale in Switzerland—the home of Schläfli and of craftsmanship in wood-carving.† It consists of six pieces, all of square cross-section with diagonally-bevelled ends. One, no. 6 in Fig. 155 (b), is plain, and must go in last in assembling the puzzle and be taken out first in dissecting it. The others are cut away as shown and their relative positions are depicted in the plan. To make an accurately-fitting model of this requires great skill, but the finished article is very attractive—far more so than the puzzle of a similar type with rectangular pieces and cubic symmetry which has had some popularity in this country.

The solid can also be thought of as a compound of three distorted octahedra—in reality square dipyramids whose faces are isosceles triangles with sides proportional to 2, $\sqrt{3}$, $\sqrt{3}$. A cardboard model is, of course, very easily made.

† This puzzle is marketed in Great Britain by Michael Martin (Toys) Ltd.

PLAN:

(a)   (b)

Key to puzzle pieces (5 lies behind 4).

FIG. 155

PUZZLE PIECES:

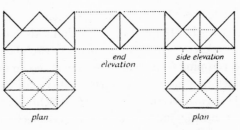

Nos. 1, 2, 3   Nos. 4, 5

FIG. 156

There are two further stellations of the rhombic dodecahedron, which are described, with a different method of construction, in 3.13 below. Further stellations of the rhombic triacontahedron are given by J. D. Ede, *Math. Gazette*, **42** (1958), 98.

The polyhedra are considered in the position in which their edges intersect at right angles. ..., r that of the inscribed sphere of the vertically regular (dual) polyhedron. $Rr = \rho^2$, since these spheres are re[ciprocal] ...ual polyhedron.

Coxeter's symbol	Our symbol	Regular polyhedron	Angle subtended by edge at centre θ	$E/\rho =$ $2r_f/r =$ $2\tan\frac12\theta$	Faces		In-:inter-:circumradius	Coxeter's symbol
$\{3,3\}$	3^3	Tetrahedron	109° 28′	2·8284				
$\{3,4\}$	3^4	Octahedron	90°	2			0·7071:1:1·2247	$\{4,3\}$
$\{3,5\}$	3^5	Icosahedron	63° 26′	1·2361			0·8507:1:1·0705	$\{5,3\}$
$\{3,\frac52\}$	$3^{5/2}$	Great icosahedron	116° 34′	3·2361	Main Re-entrant		0·5257:1:2·8025	$\{\frac52,3\}$
$\{5,\frac52\}$	$5^{5/2}$	Great dodecahedron	63° 26′	1·2361	Main Re-entrant		0·8507:1:1·9021	$\{\frac52,5\}$

Archimedean polyhedron

Coxeter's symbol	Our symbol	Regular polyhedron	Angle subtended by edge at centre θ	$E/\rho = 2\tan\frac12\theta$	Faces		ϕ_a	ϕ_b	ϕ_c
$t\{3,3\}$	3.6^2	Truncated tetrahedron	50° 28′	0·9418	6–6 6–3	5657	112° 53′	33° 34½′	
$\left\{3 \atop 4\right\}$	$(3.4)^2$	Cuboctahedron	60°	1·1547			109° 28′	70° 32′	
$t\{3,4\}$	4.6^2	Truncated octahedron	36° 52′	0·6667	6–6 6–4	3536	83° 37′	48° 11½′	
$t\{4,3\}$	3.8^2	Truncated cube	32° 39′	0·5858	8–8 8–3		117° 12′	31° 24′	
$r\left\{3 \atop 4\right\}$	3.4^3	Rhombicuboctahedron	41° 53′	0·7654	4–4 3–4	-4) -4)	115° 16′	81° 34⅔′	
$t\left\{3 \atop 4\right\}$	$4.6.8$	Truncated cuboctahedron	24° 55′	0·4419	8–4 8–6 6–4		87° 12′	55° 1½′	37° 46½′
$s\left\{3 \atop 4\right\}$	$3^4.4$	Snub cube	43° 41′	0·8018	4–3 3–3	3) -4)	114° 48½′	80° 46′	
$\left\{3 \atop 5\right\}$	$(3.5)^2$	Icosidodecahedron	36°	0·6498			116° 34′	63° 26′	
$t\{3,5\}$	5.6^2	Truncated icosahedron	23° 17′	0·4120	6–6 6–5		68° 37′	55° 41½′	
$t\{5,3\}$	3.10^2	Truncated dodecahedron	19° 24′	0·3416	10–10 10–3		119° 3′	30° 28½′	
$r\left\{3 \atop 5\right\}$	$3.4.5.4$	Rhombicosi dodecahedron	25° 52′	0·4595	5–4 3–4	-4) -5)	118° 16′	86° 59′	67° 46′
$t\left\{3 \atop 5\right\}$	$4.6.10$	Truncated icosidodecahedron	15° 6′	0·2653	10–4 10–6 6–4		89° 0′	58° 14′	32° 46′
$s\left\{3 \atop 5\right\}$	$3^4.5$	Snub dodecahedron	26° 49′	0·4769	5–3 3–3	3) -5)	118° 8′	67° 28′	
$t\{2,n\}$	$4^2.n$	Archimedean prism	$\tan^{-1}\{\sin(\pi/n)\}$	$2\sin(\pi/n)$	4–n 4–4	$\pi/n)$ $/n)$	$\cos\alpha = \sin^2(\pi/n)$		
$s\left\{2 \atop n\right\}$	$3^3.n$	Archimedean antiprism	$\tan^{-1}\{2\sin(\pi/2n)\}$	$4\sin(\pi/2n)$	3–n 3–3	$2n)$ $/2n)$	$\cos\beta = \frac12 - \cos(\pi/n)$		

3.10. Regular Compounds

If a regular polyhedron and its dual are placed together with their edges bisecting each other at right angles, as explained in 3.2, a regular compound is formed. There are five of these:

(1) two tetrahedra—Kepler's 'stella octangula';
(2) cube+octahedron;
(3) dodecahedron+icosahedron;
(4) great dodecahedron+small stellated dodecahedron;
(5) great icosahedron+great stellated dodecahedron.

Of these, (4) has the great dodecahedron entirely inside the small stellated dodecahedron (this can be made with the small stellated dodecahedron in wire); the other four are shown below, and also in Plate 1 b.

3.10.1. Stella octangula (two tetrahedra)

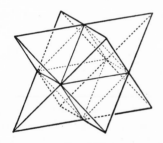

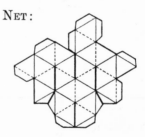

Net:

Fig. 157   Fig. 158

Cut outline and all heavy lines; score plain lines on the front, dotted lines on the back. Since tabs cannot be added as usual to alternate edges, all necessary tabs are shown.

The solid common to the two solids is an octahedron.

The solid which contains the two solids is a cube.

The edges of the stella octangula are diagonals of the faces of the cube and meet in pairs at the vertices of the octahedron.

3.10.2. Cube plus octahedron

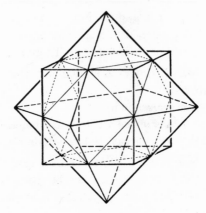

Fɪɢ. 159

Nᴇᴛ:

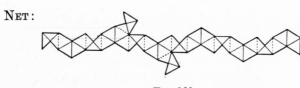

Fɪɢ. 160

Score all dotted lines on the *back*.

The solid common to the two solids is a *cuboctahedron*.

The solid which contains the two solids is a *rhombic dodeca-hedron*, and the edges of the compound solid are the diagonals of its faces.

3.10.3. Dodecahedron plus icosahedron

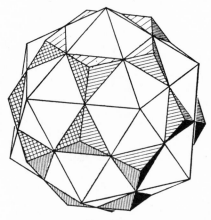

FIG. 161

NET : The solid is most easily constructed by adding triangular pyramids to an icosahedron. Twenty pyramids are required: the net for each is given. The marked edges are half the icosahedral edges; slots must be cut in each face of the icosahedron as shown and the tabs stuck down on the inside *before* the icosahedron is assembled.

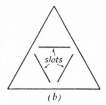

(a)   (b)

FIG. 162

The solid common to the two solids is an *icosidodecahedron*; the solid which contains the two solids is a *rhombic triacontahedron*; the edges of the compound solid are the diagonals of its faces.

3.10.4. Great icosahedron plus great stellated dodecahedron

FIG. 163

Fig. 164 shows the parts of the faces of the two solids which appear on the outside of the compound, in one diagram and in their correct proportion. The solid is most easily constructed by adding the vertices of the great icosahedron to a completed great stellated dodecahedron. To do this requires twelve B units as shown in Fig. 165. Twenty A units make up the visible parts of the dodecahedron, but there is no need to cut out the triangular nicks from the corners; it is best, however, to mark their position.

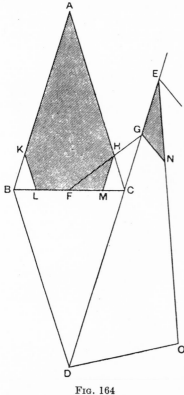

Fig. 164

$AB = AC = BD = CD.$ $\angle BAC = 36°$;
$BF = FC = CG = GE = FH,$
$BK = KL = MH = HC = HG = GN$;
$DO = BC$; $\angle CGN = 60° = \angle CDO,$
$\angle GEN = 22° 14'.$

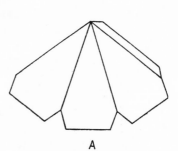

A

20 of these required. Score
internal lines before folding

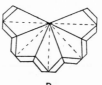

B

12 of these required. Score
full lines on front, dotted
lines on back.

Fig. 165

It is an interesting fact about this compound that if it is placed
with two trihedral vertices uppermost, in a horizontal line, the
remaining vertices fall into horizontal planes containing 6, 4, 8,
4, 6, 2 vertices respectively. Reciprocally, the planes of the faces
will meet in sets of 6, 4, 8, 4, 6 in points of a vertical line.

3.10.5. There are also sets of interpenetrating regular solids which are fitted together with the symmetry of another regular solid of higher order. They are five in number, and can be seen in Plate 1 *b*.

(1) Two tetrahedra in a cube (stella octangula).
(2) Five tetrahedra in a dodecahedron (two enantiomorphs).
(3) Ten tetrahedra in a dodecahedron (these two combined).
(4) Five cubes in a dodecahedron.
(5) Five octahedra containing an icosahedron (dual of (4)).

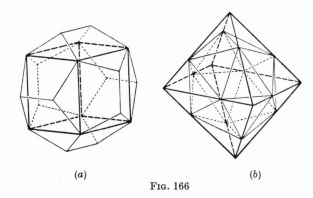

(a)   (b)

FIG. 166

Apart from the stella octangula already discussed, the starting-point for these compounds is the pair of dual figures above which show the cube in the dodecahedron and the icosahedron in the octahedron. (These figures themselves can be constructed from wire, wooden slats, or 'Perspex' strips and thread. See Plate 3 *c*.)†

The sides of the octahedron are divided in golden section; two such icosahedra can be inscribed, or alternatively two octahedra can be circumscribed to the selected planes of the icosahedron, making five in all. Five cubes of the type shown can be inscribed in the dodecahedron; each cube can be replaced by two tetrahedra as in a stella octangula; five of these ten tetrahedra can then be chosen so as to have one vertex at each dodecahedral vertex.

† See also W. Hope-Jones, *Math. Gazette*, **26** (1942), 44, 45, figs. 5 and 6.

3.10.6. Five cubes in a dodecahedron

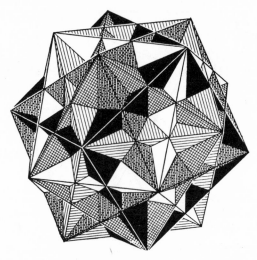

FIG. 167

The edges of the cubes lie by fives on the faces of the dodecahedron forming star-pentagons; each edge is thus divided by two other edges in golden section.

The solid common to the cubes as a whole is bounded by thirty rhombi, one on each cube face, and is thus a *rhombic triacontahedron.*

The edges of these cubes can be grouped to form equilateral triangles, ordinary pentagons, and star pentagons, besides the squares which are the cube faces. By taking different combinations of these figures, several stellated Archimedean polyhedra can be formed. Full details can be found in Coxeter, op. cit., pp. 440–3.

Construction of net of five cubes

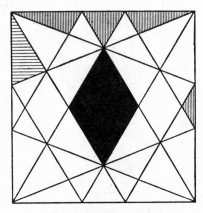

FIG. 168

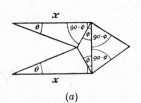

(a)

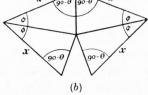

(b)

FIG. 169

$$\frac{x}{\text{Cube edge}} = \frac{3-\sqrt5}{2} = 0\cdot382; \qquad \tan\theta = \frac{3-\sqrt5}{2};$$

$$\theta = 20°\ 54'; \qquad \tan\phi = \frac{\sqrt5-1}{2} = 0\cdot618; \qquad \phi = 31°\ 43'.$$

The intersections of a cube-face with the other faces are shown
in Fig. 168; the solid rhombus is a face of the inscribed rhombic
triacontahedron; the shaded portions are external faces of the
solid compound and form parts of the net. The vertically
shaded portions of four faces fit together to form Fig. 169 (a),
and the horizontally shaded portions Fig. 169 (b). The whole
net is composed of sixty portions like (a) and thirty portions
like (b).

PLATE 1

a. The nine regular solids

b. Regular compounds

Back Row: 5 tetrahedra (*left*), 2 tetrahedra, 10 tetrahedra, cube+octahedron, 5 tetrahedra (*right*)

Front Row: 5 cubes, icosahedron+dodecahedron, great dodecahedron+great icosahedron, 5 octahedra

PLATE 2

a. The thirteen Archimedean solids
(Facially regular)

b. The thirteen Archimedean duals
(Vertically regular)

PLATE 3

a. Dissected block, ellipsoid, sectioned cone

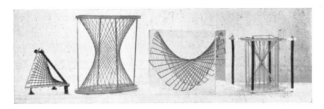

b. Ruled surfaces ('Perspex')

1 and 3. Hyperbolic paraboloid: 2 and 4 hyperboloid; no. 4 adjustable

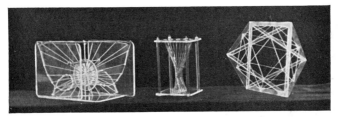

c. Half-twist surface, quartic with two double lines, icosahedron in octahedron

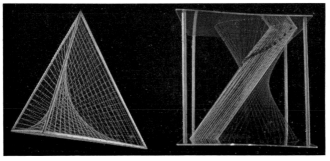

d. Six reguli in a tetrahedron, twisted cubic common to cylinder, hyperboloid, and cone

PLATE 4

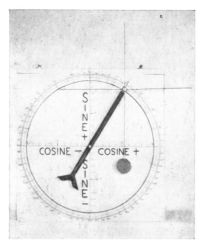

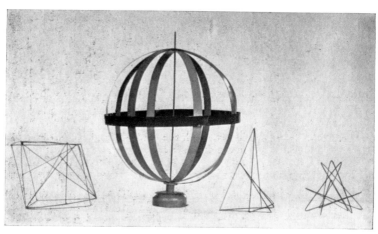

b. A group of linkages

a. Sine and cosine board

c. Models of wire and strapping

Orthocentric tetrahedron, armillary sphere, Desargues's figure, double-six

3.10.7. Five octahedra about an icosahedron

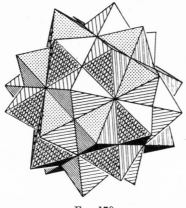

FIG. 170

The vertices of the octahedra form an icosidodecahedron; the edges are divided in golden section by other edges; the triangular faces lie two by two on the triangular faces of the inscribed icosahedron.

Construction of net. We begin by considering the section of the solid by the plane of a single face. This is shown in Fig. 171: there are two octahedral faces circumscribed to each icosahedral face, so that the section consists of two equilateral triangles. Four of the shaded portions of the section meet at each vertex of the solid; three of these vertices stand above every triangular face of one octahedron. Hence, to make the solid, begin by constructing an octahedron and attach on each face a set of three vertices whose net is given above. This can be done by slotting the octahedral face as shown, and attaching the tabs to the inside of the slots before the octahedron is assembled. The faces of the octahedron must be slotted alternately as in the figure and as in its mirror-image.

SECTION BY PLANE OF OCTAHEDRON:

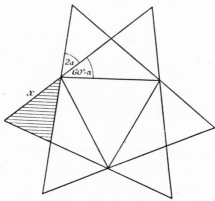

FIG. 171

$\alpha = 22°\ 14'$; $x = 0·382 \times$ octahedral edge.

THREE-VERTEX NET:

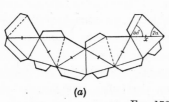

(a)

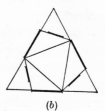

(b)

FIG. 172

Dotted lines scored on back. Slots marked with heavy lines; slots on edges can be cut where the octahedral net permits.

3.10.8. Five tetrahedra in a dodecahedron

Fig. 173

The solid common to the five tetrahedra, whose vertices are at the five-sided 'dimples', is an icosahedron, related to the outer dodecahedron in the same way as the inscribed icosahedron in the great stellated dodecahedron. The lines of intersection of tetrahedral planes are parts of edges of this same great stellated dodecahedron, and parts of diagonals joining its vertices.

The compound exists in two enantiomorphic forms; if the two are put together we have a compound of ten tetrahedra, of which two have a vertex coinciding with each vertex of the dodecahedron.

Construction of net of five tetrahedra. Consider first the section by a single face. Three other vertices lie in its plane, and the section is as shown, the sides of the equilateral triangles being divided in golden section.

Three pieces similar to the shaded portion meet at each vertex of the solid and sixty such pieces form its whole exterior surface. One of the tetrahedra can be made solid and the other four added to it. The first added tetrahedron will be antipodally

placed with respect to one of the vertices of the first tetrahedron; three of its planes will have sections as shown in
Fig. 174 (*b*), and the fourth will be the whole triangle with a

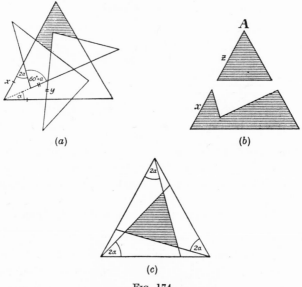

(*a*)   (*b*)

(*c*)

Fig. 174

(*a*) $\alpha = 22^\circ\ 14'$; $x = 0.382 \times$ tetrahedral edge; $y = 0.437x$.

(*b*) Section by planes of tetrahedron antipodal to vertex A;
$z = \frac{1}{2} \times$ edge. Other measurements as in previous diagram. The
three upper sections form a trihedron which fits on a face of the
first tetrahedron.

(*c*) Section of plane by antipodal trihedron.

triangle of half the side removed to fit over the point of the
other tetrahedron; this is shown in Fig. 174 (*c*).

Construction of solid. To make the solid, therefore, we
proceed as follows:

(1) Construct a single tetrahedron of the five. Mark one of
its faces as in Fig. 174 (*c*) and cut slots in part of the sides
of the shaded triangle. Mark the others as in Fig. 174 (*b*)
and cut slots in part of the 'zigzag' edges.

(2) Construct a trihedron of three pieces like the upper half
of Fig. 174 (*b*) and fit it on the base of the first tetrahedron.

(3) Construct the net below (Fig. 175): place the point of the first tetrahedron through the triangular hole and fit the tabs through the slots in the faces.

(4) The remaining twelve vertices now fit on in chains of four; the net of one vertex is given.

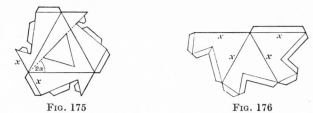

FIG. 175　　　　　　　　　　FIG. 176

The tabs shown are not all needed, but it is best to provide them, and they can be easily cut off if not required. There is no simple way of deciding which will be required and which will not.

3.10.9. Ten tetrahedra in a dodecahedron

FIG. 177

If the two enantiomorphic solids formed by the five tetrahedra are put together, the above compound results. The planes of the tetrahedral faces coincide two by two, so that the compound has twenty faces in all, the same number as the five-compound. In the diagram (Fig. 177) the faces are shaded to correspond with those of the previous diagram.

Construction of net of ten tetrahedra. Consider the section by a single face shown in Fig. 178. It consists of two interlaced equilateral triangles (faces of two tetrahedra). Five pieces similar to the double-shaded portion form a pentahedral

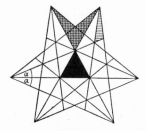

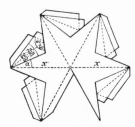

FIG. 178

FIG. 179. Dotted lines must be scored on the back, solid lines on the front. $x = 0{\cdot}437 \times$ tetrahedral edge; $\alpha = 22° 14'$.

'dimple' on each dodecahedral face; the spaces between are filled with four pieces similar to the single-shaded portion. Thus the solid can be made of sixty double-shaded portions and 120 single-shaded. The best way to make it is to build it on a stout tetrahedron out of twelve pieces similar to that shown in Fig. 179. (The inner solid triangle is a face of the inscribed icosahedron.)

3.11. DELTAHEDRA

This name is proposed as a convenient one for the class of polyhedra whose faces are all equilateral triangles. They are the easiest solids to make, since their nets are parts of the plane tessellation of equilateral triangles 3^6 (2.9.1). Beginners who would find difficulty in constructing any of the Archimedean solids can make deltahedra with ease.

There are eight convex deltahedra, as has been recently shown by Freudenthal and van der Waerden.† They are the tetrahedron, octahedron, and icosahedron: the triangular and pentagonal dipyramids: and three other solids illustrated below

† *Simon Stevin*, **25** (1947), pp. 115–21.

with sixteen, fourteen, and twelve faces respectively. If names are required they would presumably have to be the heccaideca-deltahedron, the tetracaidecadeltahedron, and the dodecadelta-hedron! These bring the number of convex polyhedra with congruent regular faces up to ten.

Of non-convex deltahedra only a few more interesting examples are described here.

(1) The three-dimensional net of the regular four-dimensional simplex or pentatope consists of a tetrahedron with four equal tetrahedra stuck on to its faces.

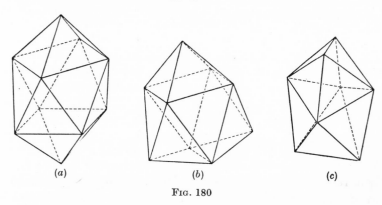

(a)   (b)   (c)

Fig. 180

(2) A cuboctahedron with square pyramids pointing *outwards* on its faces is merely an octahedron, but if the pyramids point *inwards* so as to meet in the centre, an interesting surface is formed which can be regarded as made up of triangles and regular diametral hexagons (see Fig. 243 (c)).

To make it, take the net of the octahedron and divide each triangle into four by joining the mid-points of the sides. Score these lines on the front and all others on the back, and join up so that all the free vertices meet in the centre. A very rigid model results.

(3) If the same is done with the net of the icosahedron an icosidodecahedron results with pentagonal dimples.

(4) Pentagonal pyramids can be described inwards or outwards on the faces of a dodecahedron. In the former case (with the planes of the original dodecahedron removed, of course)

a deltahedron results with three equilateral triangles in each of its planes. It is one of the fifty-nine stellations of the icosahedron,† and has been described in 3.6.4 above.

(5) As a class activity tetrahedra and octahedra can be fixed on the faces of a basic polyhedron, which may be a tetrahedron, octahedron, or icosahedron, or indeed any suitable convex

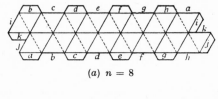

(a) $n = 8$

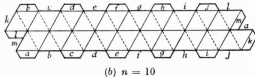

(b) $n = 10$

Fig. 181. Dotted lines must be scored on the back. The tabs are joined to the edges with the same letter.

deltahedron. The solids that result are amusing but not of great mathematical interest. In the case of octahedra on the faces of an icosahedron the solid is only distinguished by narrow fissures from number (3) above.

(6) To be included here are the rotating rings of tetrahedra described by Coxeter in his revised edition of Rouse Ball's *Mathematical Recreations and Essays*, p. 153. These consist of n tetrahedra, each joined to its two neighbours by a pair of opposite edges to form a ring ($n \geqslant 6$). If $n \geqslant 8$ the ring can rotate, and if $n \geqslant 22$ it can be knotted. The nets for the cases $n = 8$ and $n = 10$ are here given. For full details the reader is referred to Rouse Ball, op. cit., pp. 153-4 and 216.

† Coxeter, DuVal, Flather, and Petrie, *The Fifty-nine Icosahedra*, University of Toronto Studies (Mathematical Series), no. 6, 1938.

3.12. Unitary Construction

An interesting method of constructing polyhedra is to build them from smaller solid units, which will usually be of more than one kind. This is a suitable method for class use where mass-production can be employed, individual units being cut from cards marked out by pricking through a master template. Very rapid production results. If it is desired to take the polyhedron to pieces again after assembly, some kind of tongue-and-slot mechanism must be devised. A cut can be made in the centre of each face in one of the forms shown (Fig. 182)—they must,

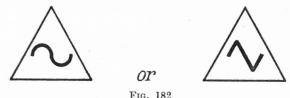

or

Fig. 182

of course, be properly aligned. The ambitious might experiment with press-studs. Stellations can be added in this way to polyhedra, and removed again to show the structure. In addition many Archimedean polyhedra can be made by adding units to a simpler solid. The most interesting results arise when some units are omitted, and also the central polyhedron itself, leaving a polyhedron with missing faces replaced by tunnels connecting with another polyhedron inside.

The simplest case is the truncated tetrahedron (3.6^2). Construct four units A as in Fig. 183. Each unit has for base a regular hexagon. Alternate sloping sides are right-angled isosceles triangles and rectangles with sides in the ratio $1:\frac{1}{2}\sqrt{2}$ ($2\sin \pi/4:1$). An equilateral triangle closes the top. The net is obvious. If four such boxes are stuck together by their rectangular faces they will form a truncated tetrahedron with a tetrahedral hollow in the interior. The tetrahedron cannot, of course, be seen unless one box is omitted. If eight are stuck together by their triangular faces, however, a truncated octahedron results with cuboidal holes where its square faces should be, leading to a cuboctahedral interior.

For the solids with octahedral symmetry there are two kinds of unit. The B-units (Fig. 184) have a resemblance to the A's, but the sloping rectangles have sides in the ratio $2 \sin \pi/6 : 1$, and are therefore squares, so that the sloping triangles are

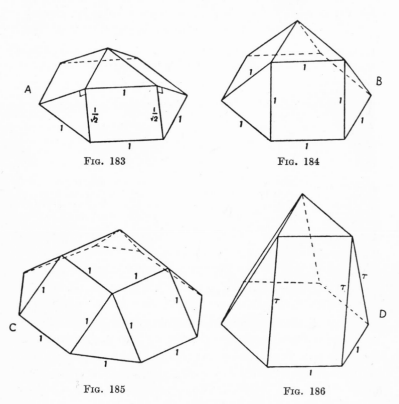

FIG. 183   FIG. 184

FIG. 185   FIG. 186

equilateral. The units are halves of cuboctahedra. Eight B's, joined by their square faces, make a truncated octahedron (4.6^2) with its square faces missing, revealing the vertices of an octahedral interior. The C-units (Fig. 185) are caps of rhombicuboctahedra (3.4^3). They have regular octagonal bases, square tops, and their sloping faces are again squares and equilateral triangles. Six C's, stuck together by their square faces, make a truncated cube (3.8^2) with a cubical interior. If now the eight B's and six C's are stuck together alternately by their triangular

faces, a beautiful solid is produced, consisting of a great rhombicuboctahedron (4.6.8) with its square faces removed, revealing
cubical holes leading to a small rhombicuboctahedron within
(3.4³). (See Fig. 188.)

The treatment of the icosahedral solids is similar. Twenty
D-units (Fig. 186) whose bases are regular hexagons, whose tops

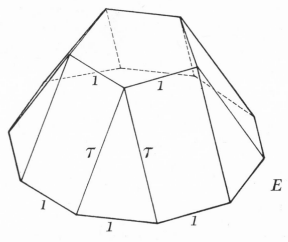

FIG. 187

are equilateral triangles, and whose sloping faces are alternately
isosceles triangles with angles 36°, 72°, 72° and rectangles with
sides in the ratio $1 : \tau$ ($2 \sin \pi/10 : 1$), if joined by rectangular faces,
form a truncated icosahedron (5.6²) with a icosahedral interior.
Twelve E-units (Fig. 187) whose sloping faces are congruent to
those of the D's, joined in the same way, make a truncated
dodecahedron (3.10²) with a dodecahedral interior. Finally, if
the D's and E's are joined alternately by their triangular faces,
a great rhombicosidodecahedron results (4.6.10), penetrated
by cuboidal holes, revealing the rhombicosidodecahedron inside
(3.4.5.4).

These two combination solids are most attractive, especially
if the B's and C's, or D's and E's, are made of differently
coloured thin card, and when a light is hung inside they make
most effective decorations.

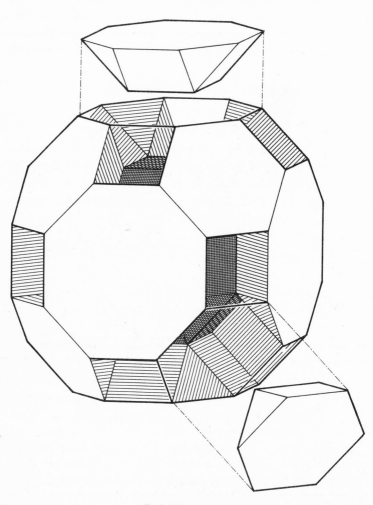

Fig. 188

TABLE II

Data relating to the regular and Archimedean polyhedra and their duals

The polyhedra are considered in the position in which their edges intersect at right angles. ρ is the radius of the *intersphere* touching these edges, R that of the circumsphere of the facially regular (Archimedean) polyhedron, r that of the inscribed sphere of the vertically regular (dual) polyhedron. $Rr = \rho^2$, since these spheres are reciprocal. E is the edge of the Archimedean polyhedron, e that of the dual. r_f is the radius of the inscribed circle of a face of the dual polyhedron.

Coxeter's symbol	Our symbol	Regular polyhedron	Angle subtended by edge at centre θ	$E/\rho =$ $2r_f/r =$ $2\tan\frac{1}{2}\theta$	Dihedral angles Faces	Dihedral angles Angles	In-:inter-:circumradius	Our symbol	Regular dual polyhedron	Dihedral angle $\pi-\theta$	e/ρ	In-:inter-:circumradius	Coxeter's symbol
$\{3,3\}$	3^3	Tetrahedron	109° 28′	2·8284		70° 32′	0·5774:1:1·7321		(Self-dual)				
$\{3,4\}$	3^4	Octahedron	90°	2		109° 28′	0·8165:1:1·4142	4^3	Cube	90°	1·4142	0·7071:1:1·2247	$\{4,3\}$
$\{3,5\}$	3^5	Icosahedron	63° 26′	1·2361		138° 11′	0·9342:1:1·1756	5^3	Dodecahedron	116° 34′	0·7639	0·8507:1:1·0705	$\{5,3\}$
$\{3,\frac{5}{2}\}$	$3^{5/2}$	Great icosahedron	116° 34′	3·2361	Main / Re-entrant	41° 49′ / 109° 28′	0·3568:1:1·9021	$(\frac{5}{2})^3$	Great stellated dodecahedron	63° 26′	5·2361	0·5257:1:2·8025	$\{\frac{5}{2},3\}$
$\{5,\frac{5}{2}\}$	$5^{5/2}$	Great dodecahedron	63° 26′	1·2361	Main / Re-entrant	63° 26′ / 116° 34′	0·5257:1:1·1756	$(\frac{5}{2})^5$	Small stellated dodecahedron	116° 34′	3·2361	0·8507:1:1·9021	$\{\frac{5}{2},5\}$

	Archimedean polyhedron						$r:\rho:R = \cos\frac{1}{2}\theta:1:\sec\frac{1}{2}\theta$	Dual (vertically regular) polyhedron			Face angles ϕ_a	ϕ_b	ϕ_c
$t\{3,3\}$	3.6^2	Truncated tetrahedron	50° 28′	0·9418	6–6 / 6–3	70° 32′ / 109° 28′	0·9045:1:1·1055	V.3.6² Triakis tetrahedron	129° 32′	3, 3, 5×0·5657	112° 53′	33° 34½′	
$\binom{3}{4}$	$(3.4)^2$	Cuboctahedron	60°	1·1547		125° 16′	0·8660:1:1·1547	V.(3.4)² Rhombic dodecahedron	120°	1·0607	109° 28′	70° 32′	
$t\{3,4\}$	4.6^2	Truncated octahedron	36° 52′	0·6667	6–6 / 6–4	109° 28′ / 125° 16′	0·9487:1:1·0541	V.4.6² Tetrakis hexahedron	143° 8′	3, 3, 4×0·3536	83° 37′	48° 11½′	
$t\{4,3\}$	3.8^2	Truncated cube	32° 39′	0·5858	8–8 / 8–3	90° / 125° 16′	0·9597:1:1·0420	V.3.8² Triakis octahedron	147° 21′	1·1716 / 1·1716 / 2	117° 12′	31° 24′	
$r\binom{3}{4}$	3.4^3	Rhombicuboctahedron	41° 53′	0·7654	4–4 / 3–4	135° / 144° 44′	0·9340:1:1·0707	V.3.4³ Trapezoidal icositetrahedron	138° 7′	0·6408 (3–4) / 0·8284 (4–4)	115° 16′	81° 34⅔′	
$t\binom{3}{4}$	$4.6.8$	Truncated cuboctahedron	24° 55′	0·4419	8–4 / 8–6 / 6–4	135° / 125° 16′ / 144° 44′	0·9765:1:1·0241	V.4.6.8 Hexakis octahedron	155° 5′	0·6408 / 0·8571 / 1·0448	87° 12′	55° 1½′	37° 46½′
$s\binom{3}{4}$	$3^4.4$	Snub cube	43° 41′	0·8018	4–3 / 3–3	142° 59′ / 153° 14′	0·9282:1:1·0773	V.3⁴.4 Pentagonal icositetrahedron	136° 19′	0·4758 (3–3) / 0·6755 (3–4)	114° 48½′	80° 46′	
$\binom{3}{5}$	$(3.5)^2$	Icosidodecahedron	36°	0·6498		142° 37′	0·9511:1:1·0515	V.(3.5)² Rhombic triacontahedron	144°	0·6910	116° 34′	63° 26′	
$t\{3,5\}$	5.6^2	Truncated icosahedron	23° 17′	0·4120	6–6 / 6–5	138° 11′ / 142° 37′	0·9794:1:1·0210	V.5.6² Pentakis dodecahedron	156° 43′	0·6776 / 0·6776 / 0·7639	68° 37′	55° 41½′	
$t\{5,3\}$	3.10^2	Truncated dodecahedron	19° 24′	0·3416	10–10 / 10–3	116° 34′ / 142° 37′	0·9857:1:1·0145	V.3.10² Triakis icosahedron	160° 36′	0·7172 / 0·7172 / 1·2361	119° 3′	30° 28½′	
$r\binom{3}{5}$	$3.4.5.4$	Rhombicosidodecahedron	25° 52′	0·4595	5–4 / 3–4	148° 17′ / 159° 6′	0·9747:1:1·0260	V.3.4.5.4 Trapezoidal hexecontahedron	154° 8′	0·3699 (3–4) / 0·5694 (3–5)	118° 16′	86° 59′	67° 46′
$t\binom{3}{5}$	$4.6.10$	Truncated icosidodecahedron	15° 6′	0·2653	10–4 / 10–6 / 6–4	148° 17′ / 142° 37′ / 159° 6′	0·9914:1:1·0087	V.4.6.10 Hexakis icosahedron	164° 54′	0·3699 / 0·5810 / 0·6833	89° 0′	58° 14′	32° 46′
$s\binom{3}{5}$	$3^4.5$	Snub dodecahedron	26° 49′	0·4769	5–3 / 3–3	152° 56′ / 164° 11′	0·9727:1:1·0280	V.3⁴.5 Pentagonal hexecontahedron	153° 11′	0·2779 (3–3) / 0·4863 (3–5)	118° 8′	67° 28′	
$t\{2,n\}$	$4^2.n$	Archimedean prism	$\tan^{-1}\{\sin(\pi/n)\}$	$2\sin(\pi/n)$	4–n / 4–4	$\pi/2$ / $\pi-2\pi/n$	$\dfrac{1}{\sqrt{\{1+\sin^2(\pi/n)\}}}:1:\sqrt{\{1+\sin^2(\pi/n)\}}$	V.4².n Dipyramid		$a\ 2\csc(2\pi/n)$ / $b\ 2\tan(\pi/n)$	$\cos\alpha=\sin^2(\pi/n)$		
$s\binom{2}{n}$	$3^3.n$	Archimedean antiprism	$\tan^{-1}\{2\sin(\pi/2n)\}$	$4\sin(\pi/2n)$	3–n / 3–3	$\sec^{-1}-\sqrt{3}\{\csc(\pi/n)+\cot(\pi/n)\}$ / $\cos^{-1}\frac{1}{3}\{1-4\cos(\pi/n)\}$	$\dfrac{1}{\sqrt{\{3-2\cos(\pi/n)\}}}:1:\sqrt{\{3-2\cos(\pi/n)\}}$	V.3³.n Trapezohedron $\lambda^2=\dfrac{1}{1+2\cos(\pi/n)}$		$a\ \lambda\csc(\pi/2n)$ / $b\ 4\lambda\sin(\pi/2n)$	$\cos\beta=\frac{1}{2}-\cos(\pi/n)$		

Incidentally, beginning with the solid tessellation of truncated octahedra, we can dissect each unit into a central octahedron and eight boxes B, then unite the B-units in pairs, and finally arrive at the tessellation of cuboctahedra and octahedra alternately. In a similar way we can derive the rhombic dodecahedral packing from the cubic via the six square pyramids. (See 3.8.3 above.)

3.13. The Stellations of the Rhombic Dodecahedron

Besides dividing the rhombic dodecahedron into twelve square pyramids, we can also divide it into units in another way. Each unit is a pyramid with vertex at the centre of the solid, and with its base coinciding with a rhombic face. The unit and its net are shown in the diagrams (Figs. 189, 190).

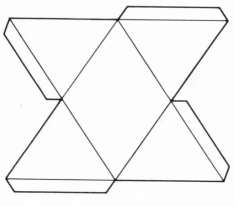

Fig. 189

Mr. Dorman Luke has recently discovered the remarkable fact that the three stellations of the rhombic dodecahedron can also be built from these units; 72 will be needed in all—12 for the rhombic dodecahedron itself, 12 more for the first stellation, and 24 each for the second and third stellations. Diagrams of all these are given (Figs. 191–3). Their complete construction from the 72 units makes an interesting project.

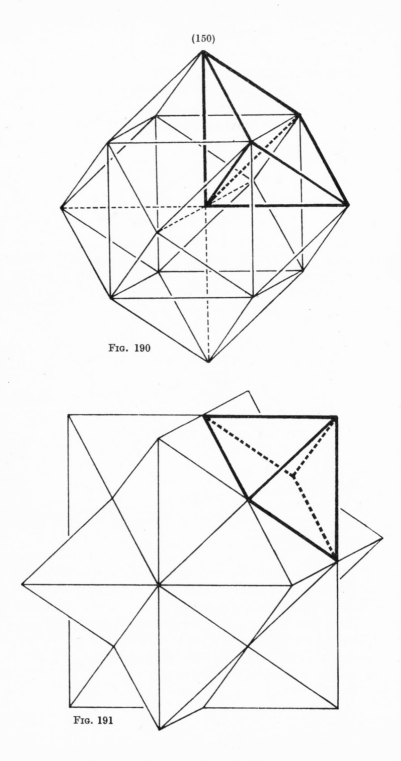

(150)

Fig. 190

Fig. 191

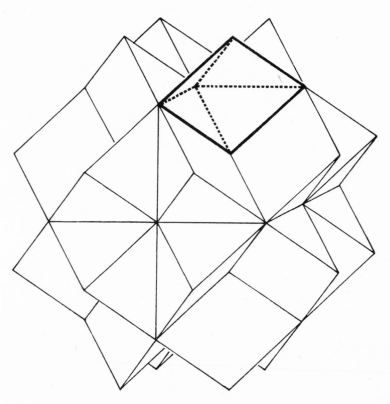

Fig. 192

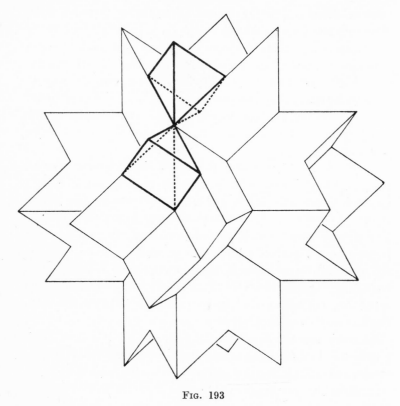

FIG. 193

3.14. PLAITING

A nineteenth-century doctor named John Gorham, of Tonbridge, Kent, discovered a most interesting method of constructing polyhedra by simply plaiting flat strips together. He published a book on the subject—*Plaited Crystal Models*—in 1888. Recently Mr. A. R. Pargeter of Southampton has developed and extended his methods, and a full account is given by him in *Math. Gazette*, **43** (1959), 88. The figures given here are taken from that article by permission. There is only space to deal with a few simple cases.

The method consists in dividing the surface of the polyhedron into quadrilaterals, either by pairing triangular faces, by using existing square or four-sided faces, by 'sectoring' faces (dividing them into triangles by joining vertices to a central point), or by a combination of these devices. Strips are then made, formed of chains of quadrilaterals, two strips crossing at each quadrilateral, and are then plaited together in the ordinary way to form the surface. The final ends of the strips are tucked under previous strands and the model is rigid and complete. The reader will learn more from making a few than from any number of words.

Paper of good quality should be used, and not card. Cut all thick lines in the nets, and crease all thin ones; ignore all dotted lines which are only inserted to show the construction of the strips. Creases must be accurate and firm. Coloured paper can be used with advantage; if strips are cut from different coloured papers most attractive models can be made. In this case the coloured strips must be stuck together as the nets indicate before beginning to plait. Since all strips are identical (except for the ends) they can be cut out together; Pargeter recommends stapling the sheets together, when scissors can be used.

In every case the *first* plait determines all that follow. This is indicated in the net; assuming that the net represents the outside, so that the main creases are away from the reader, we begin by putting the faces marked *O over* the faces marked *U* (under). Then each strip goes over and under alternately, and at every vertex if we rotate in one direction the strips either step up continuously or step down continuously. A correct start ensures that at the finish there will be slots to tuck the ends in.

The experimenter is advised to begin with some simple models. Fig. 194 shows a *cube*; the net can be very easily cut from squared paper. Fig. 195 shows a simple net for folding a tetrahedron; the triangles marked 'X' are not necessary, but make the model more rigid. A firmer tetrahedron with a sectored face results from Fig. 199; Fig. 198 shows a tetrahedron with all its faces sectored. Figs. 196 and 200 give simple octahedra; Fig. 201 an octahedron with a pair of sectored faces. Fig. 197 is the icosahedron. All these nets with equilateral triangles can be cut from isometric paper which is ruled in equilateral triangles.

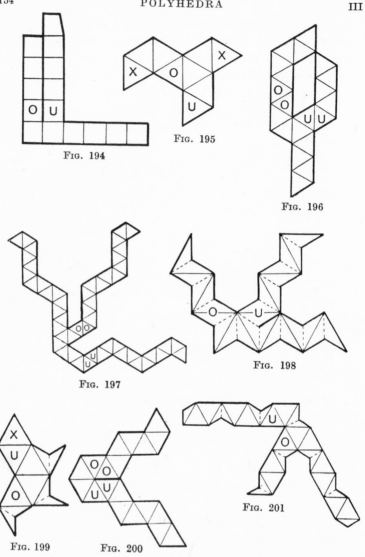

FIG. 194

FIG. 195

FIG. 196

FIG. 197

FIG. 198

FIG. 199

FIG. 200

FIG. 201

Figs. 202–5 form an interesting series. The nets are similarly constructed; only the basic rhombi and the folding schemes are different. In Fig. 202 we have a 60° rhombus folded along a long diagonal; the result is an octahedron with all faces sectored. In Fig. 203 we have squares, leading to a cube; again, all faces

are sectored. In Fig. 204 we have rhombi with angles of 70° 32′
(diagonals √2:1); we fold *between* the rhombi: result, a rhombic
dodecahedron. Finally, in Fig. 205 the rhombi have angles of
120° (i.e. they are congruent to those in Fig. 202 but joined by

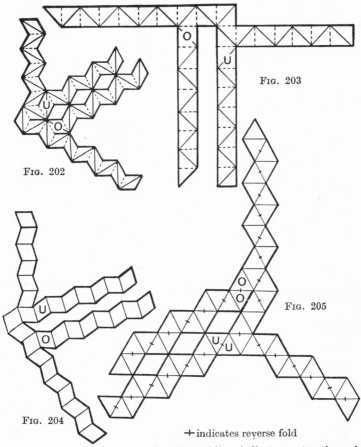

FIG. 203

FIG. 202

FIG. 205

FIG. 204

╋ indicates reverse fold

Dotted lines indicate construction only

the other edges); here we fold along the common edges and
make reverse creases along the *short* diagonals; the result is a
stella octangula. This is not easy to plait; the experimenter
may well prefer to have a solid stella octangula of the same
size on which to operate at first! Do not lose heart—it *does* work
and a very rigid model results. We could also make the angles

83° 37′ in Fig. 204 and fold in addition along the short diagonals, to produce a tetrakis hexahedron; similarly if we make the obtuse angles 117° 14′ in Fig. 202 and fold in addition along the common edges, we obtain a triakis octahedron.

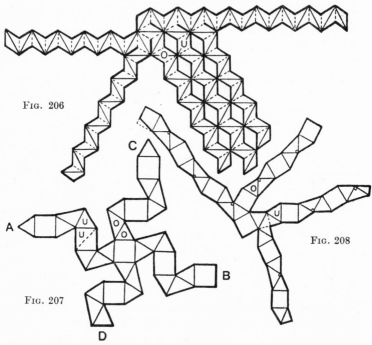

FIG. 206

FIG. 207

FIG. 208

There is an exactly similar series for the icosahedral group of polyhedra. Fig. 206 is the net for the icosahedron itself. A short table of the various modifications follows:

Solid	Obtuse angle of rhombus	Crease
Icosahedron	120°	Long diagonals only
Triakis icosahedron	119° 3′	Long diagonals and edges
Rhombic triacontahedron	116° 34′	Edges only
Pentakis dodecahedron	111° 24′	Short diagonals and edges
Dodecahedron	108°	Short diagonals only
Great dodecahedron	108°	Long diagonals, and edges reversed

Those who have progressed so far will have no difficulty in constructing nets for other solids. Figs. 207 and 208 give two ways of folding the cuboctahedron, by way of example. A

full account of the system can be found in Pargeter's article
mentioned above.

3.15. MISCELLANEOUS

We shall complete this chapter with a few polyhedral models
of interest.

3.15.1. Hexagonal section of a cube.
It is a familiar
piece of work in Elementary Geometry to prove that the face
exposed by a plane section of a cube through XY, $X'Y'$ (see
Fig. 209) is a regular hexagon. A model which shows this is

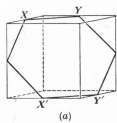
(a)

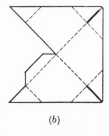
(b)

FIG. 209

Cut through the thick lines; score all dotted lines. The triangles in
the model are all double.

easily constructed from a square of card as shown; the hexagon
must be made separately, with tabs on all its edges.

All regular solids have such a central section which is a regular
h-gon; where for the tetrahedron, $h = 4$, giving a square, as seen
in a popular puzzle (cf. 4.9.1 b); for the cube and octahedron,
$h = 6$; for 3^5 and 5^3, $h = 10$; for $3^{\frac{5}{2}}$ and $(\frac{5}{2})^3$, $h = \frac{10}{3}$; for $5^{\frac{5}{2}}$ and
$(\frac{5}{2})^5$, $h = 6$.

3.15.2. Prince Rupert's cubes.
What is the largest cube
that can be made to pass through a given cube? Suppose we
have a cube of wood. The problem is to cut a channel through
it of square section, the original cube remaining in one piece.
What is the largest side of such a square?

Surprisingly enough, the side is greater than that of the
original cube, and the channel is not parallel to a main diagonal
of the cube. It can be proved that a cube whose side is less
than $\frac{3}{4}\sqrt{2} = 1 \cdot 06065$ times the side of the original cube can be
made to pass through, and the channel has its maximum cross-

section when it is in the position shown in the figure (Fig. 210).†
It is easy to make a model of this, but it must be very accurate
if a cube larger than the original is in fact able to go through.

3.15.3. Solid tessellations. Just as there is a finite
number of ways of filling a plane with a pattern of regular
polygons, regularly arranged, so there is a finite number of
ways of filling space with regular or Archimedean polyhedra.

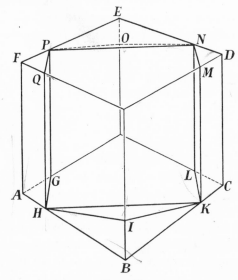

FIG. 210

$$AG = AH = CK = CL = DM = DN = FP = FQ = \tfrac{1}{4}AB.$$
$$BI = EO = \tfrac{3}{16}AB.$$

Where there is only one kind of solid we have the following
five tessellations (the second index gives the number surrounding an edge):

   (1) Cubes $(4^3)^4$;

   (2) Triangular prisms $(3.4^2)^{6,4}$;

   (3) Hexagonal prisms $(6.4^2)^{3,4}$;

   (4) Rhombic dodecahedra $\{V(3.4)^2\}^3$;

   (5) Truncated octahedra $(4.6^2)^3$.

† See *German Encyclopaedia* III, Abt. 9, Zacharias, p. 1133; Cantor, *Geschichte*,
vol. 3, p. 528; D. J. E. Schrek, *Scripta Mathematica*, **16** (1950), 73 f., 261–7.

Of these, number (1) is very familiar, and number (4) is important, as the arrangement of the centres of the rhombic dodecahedra is one of the two ways (cubic) of close-packing of spheres. The other way (hexagonal close-packing) gives rise to a tessellation of *trapezo-rhombic dodecahedra*. For details, see Rouse Ball, op. cit., pp. 148 ff., or Lines, *Solid Geometry*, p. 146 and pp. 205–7, and section 4.7 in the next chapter.

If there are two or more kinds of solid in the tessellation, and they are similarly arranged about every edge, we have only three more tessellations, viz.:

(6) Tetrahedra and octahedra $\{(3^3).(3^4)\}^2$;

(7) Tetrahedra and truncated tetrahedra $(3^3).(3.6^2)^3$;

(8) Octahedra and cuboctahedra $(3^4).\{(3.4)^2\}^2$.

The construction of these various tessellations is very suitable for class activity.

3.15.4. Four dimensions. The regular figure in four-dimensional space is called a *polytope*, or rather a *four-dimensional polytope*, as the word polytope is general. There are sixteen such, six convex and ten stellated. The net of the simplest, the *pentatope*, has been given above (3.11 (1)), but a better idea of it is obtained from a three-dimensional projection of its edges. This is made simply by joining every vertex of a regular tetrahedron to a fifth vertex, either outside it or inside, for example, at its centre (Fig. 211 (b)). Compare the plane projection of the regular tetrahedron (Fig. 211 (a)).

The next most simple polytope is the *tesseract*, or *hypercube*, which has eight cubic cells. A projection of this can be made in several ways, but two simple ways are shown. We may either take two cubes, slightly displaced from coincidence, and join corresponding vertices by parallel lines (oblique parallel projection, Fig. 211 (e)), or take two cubes, one slightly smaller than the other and centrally placed inside it, and join corresponding vertices by concurrent lines (perspective, Fig. 211 (f)). Compare the two ways of showing a cube in a plane diagram (Figs. 211 (c) and (d)). Projections of all the convex polytopes in four dimensions are given in Coxeter's *Regular Polytopes*.

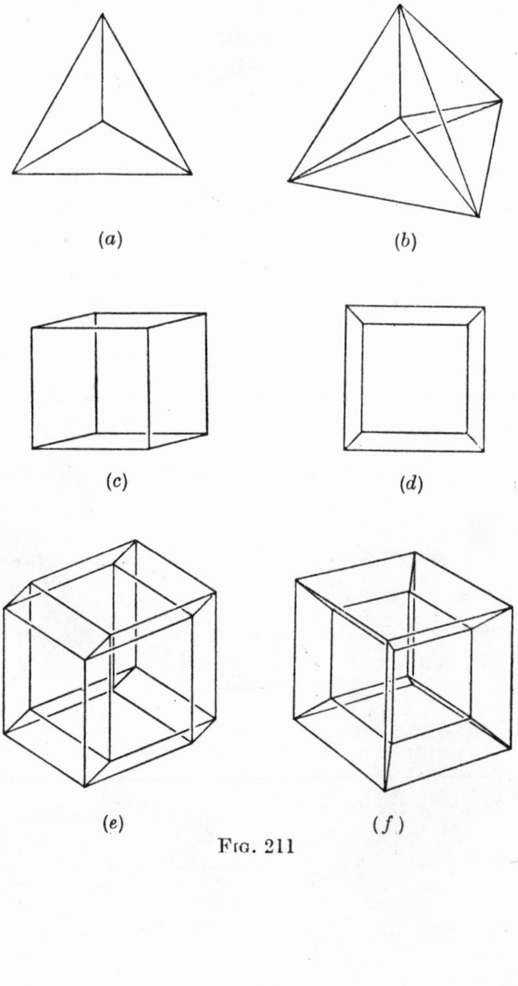

(a)

(b)

(c)

(d)

(e)

(f)

Fig. 211

OTHER MODELS IN SOLID GEOMETRY

4.1. WIRE MODELS

A NUMBER of configurations of solid geometry are of such frequent occurrence and intrinsic interest that a permanent model is worth constructing. The simplest configurations involve only the incidence of lines and points and are conveniently made in wire.

The technique of making a wire model is simple provided certain precautions are taken. The wire used can be bare soft iron wire, which is easily bent into any required shape. Iron wire can also be obtained covered with coloured plastic insulation at electrical shops. This is a useful form of wire and is obtainable in various colours. It has the advantage that it is easy to bend, cut, and solder, and needs no painting. On the other hand, a model made from it will be distorted by handling, and straight lines will not retain their straightness for very long. Hard steel piano wire gives slightly more trouble in construction, but produces a more robust finished article. Wire of fairly fine gauge, cut into reasonable lengths, can be obtained from most good ironmongers. To bend it, first soften it in a flame. Clean the ends with emery before soldering, and use Baker's fluid which gives more certain results than the usual flux. For thicker lines, steel knitting-needles can be used. To colour the wires, use glossy, coloured dope such as is sold for covering model aircraft.

We shall give three examples of such models, but of course the possibilities are unlimited; in particular all the polyhedra can be made with wire edges, though the plane faces are not shown in such a model and, for example, the great dodecahedron and the icosahedron are indistinguishable.

4.1.1. Desargues's configuration. The properties of this important figure are most easily seen in a model, including the proof of the existence of the configuration in space, and the complete symmetry of the figure, every point being a possible vertex of perspective and every line a possible axis. The figure is shown below (Fig. 212), and in Plate 4c; it can be coloured either to show a pair of triangles, their axis and vertex of perspective; or, alternatively, to show that the ten lines fall into two sets of five, each of which forms a skew pentagon inscribed in the other.

4.1.2. The orthocentric tetrahedron. This is another of the important figures of solid geometry. It can be constructed

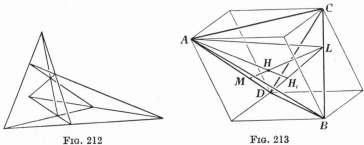

FIG. 212   FIG. 213

together with its circumscribing parallelepiped as shown. If this is done the sides of the tetrahedron, the sides of the parallelepiped, the altitudes, and mutual perpendiculars should be coloured differently. It requires care and patience to get the wires soldered together at the corners. The parallelepiped, which in this case is a rhomboid, should first be made of twelve equal pieces of wire, then the diagonals can be measured and the tetrahedron added, and finally the other lines.

AL, DL are perpendicular to BC; AH_1 is perpendicular to DL and therefore an altitude of the tetrahedron. LM is the mutual perpendicular between AD and BC. H_1 is the orthocentre of the face BCD and H that of the tetrahedron. Further altitudes and mutual perpendiculars through H can be added if desired (with rapidly increasing difficulty!). Those shown are the minimum necessary to show the properties of the figure.

4.1.3. The double-six. The general theorem of the double-six is due to Schläfli, and the configuration, like the proof, is somewhat complicated. A special case, however, in which the result is obvious, is worth constructing as it leads to an elegant figure.

The starting-point of the theorem is the fact that there is just one transversal to two skew lines through every point in space. This leads to the consideration of the set of transversals of three skew lines, forming a ruled quadric surface (see 4.3 below). A fourth line not lying in this quadric will meet it in two points; hence there are just two transversals to four general skew lines. Now suppose we take five skew lines a, b, c, d, e with a common transversal ζ. There will be one other common transversal to every set of four

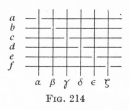

Fig. 214

of them. Let the common transversal of $bcde$ be α; of $acde$, β; of $abde$, γ; of $abce$, δ; and $abcd$, ϵ. Then the five lines $\alpha\beta\gamma\delta\epsilon$ have a common transversal f. That is to say, we have two sets of six lines, each member of each set meeting five members of the other set. To prove this, we shall ignore degenerate cases in which certain lines coincide, which are best treated analytically.

Suppose f is the common transversal, other than a, of $\beta\gamma\delta\epsilon$. We must prove that f meets α.

Choose four points on ζ, and three on each of the lines a–e, none of them being points of intersection of the lines so far defined. Through these nineteen points a unique cubic surface C can be drawn. Since it has four points in common with ζ, it contains ζ entirely, which gives it a fourth point in common with each of the five lines a–e. Hence it contains each of these lines entirely, and hence, again for the same reason, it contains each of the five lines $\alpha\beta\gamma\delta\epsilon$. Finally, C contains f, since it meets it in the four points $f\beta$, $f\gamma$, $f\delta$, $f\epsilon$. That is, to recapitulate, all twelve lines lie on C.

Suppose now that f does not meet α. Then there is a second transversal of $\alpha\beta\gamma\delta$, different from e and f, which we may call g. g meets C in the four points $g\alpha$, $g\beta$, $g\gamma$, $g\delta$ and therefore lies in C. That is to say that four transversals of $\beta\gamma\delta$, viz. a, e, f, g, lie entirely in C. But this would mean that every transversal of a, e, f, g would meet C in four points and lie entirely in C, i.e. the quadric defined by $\beta\gamma\delta$ would belong to C, so that C would consist of this quadric and a plane. But we have supposed at the outset that no four of a, b, c, d, e lie in the same quadric, so that at least two of them must lie in the plane, which is not so. Hence our supposition is false, and f must meet α.†

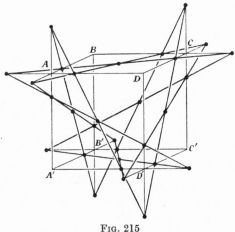

FIG. 215

So much for the theorem; now for an actual model of a specially symmetrical case.

Consider a cube $ABCDA'B'C'D'$. Select four of its vertices alternately, at the vertices of a regular tetrahedron, for example, $ACB'D'$. Three edges pass through each vertex; produce these edges outwards through the vertex to equal distances, thus obtaining twelve points. Join each of these points to the two points which lie diametrically opposite to it in the two faces in which it lies. The result is a double-six of lines possessing the symmetry of the regular tetrahedron. Every line lies in a face and meets five other lines, at the centre of the face, and at the points where it meets the four edges of the face. The only line of the second set which it does not meet is the line perpendicular to it in the opposite face. Thus a is perpendicular to α, b to β, and so on. In the general case they are polar lines

† This method of proof is due to Hilbert, and it is included here because there is no easily accessible account in English.

with respect to a quadric; here this quadric is the imaginary sphere with centre at the centre of the cube and $(\text{radius})^2 = -a^2$, where the side of the cube is $2a$.

To construct the model, shown in Fig. 215, notice that the lines form three sets of four, connected only by their ends, in

FIG. 216

the form of a 'double hair-pin'. The three sets are identical (see Fig. 216). We therefore construct three of these units—skew quadrilaterals with all their plane angles equal—and fit

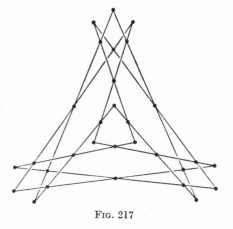

FIG. 217

them together to form the double-six (Fig. 217).

4.1.4. Other configurations of lines in space. There are unlimited possibilities of figures composed of lines in three-dimensional space, but there are a few of geometrical interest which the reader may care to investigate for himself; e.g.

(a) Möbius tetrads: two tetrahedra arranged so that each vertex of either lies on a face of the other. The figure contains eight points and eight planes, but many other points will be needed in its construction.

(b) Reye's configuration; projectively equivalent to the figure consisting of the twelve edges of a cube and its four cube-diagonals, in which three points are at infinity. This has twelve points, three on a line; and sixteen lines meeting in fours at the points.

(c) The projections of the regular four-dimensional polytopes. These are figured in Coxeter's *Regular Polytopes*, and in Hilbert's *Anschauliche Geometrie*. (English translation: Hilbert and Cohn-Vossen, *Geometry and the Imagination*.)

4.2. WOODEN MODELS

Of course any model made of wire could also be made with wooden sticks cemented together, or with plastic cocktail-sticks, or the slats of cane from dinner-mats. 'Evostik' is a suitable adhesive for use with these. Polyhedra can be made by constructing their edges, and, if desired, sheeting of paper or thin card can be cemented on the framework to show the planes.

This section however is a convenient place to collect together a few examples of models that can be made out of solid wood. We shall describe three such which can be made by anyone who can handle a lathe. The first two are shown in Plate 3 a.

4.2.1. A dissected cuboid. In order to prove that the volume of a tetrahedron is $\frac{1}{3}$ base-area × height, it is usual to proceed by showing that all pyramids of the same height and the same base-area are equal in volume. Unlike the situation in two dimensions, this cannot be done by dissection, but an argument which is equivalent to integration has to be employed.

When once this has been proved, it only remains to show that the formula holds for one such pyramid. This can most easily be done by dissecting a cuboid into six tetrahedra of equal volume.

Consider the cuboid $ABCDA'B'C'D'$ in Fig. 218. First make

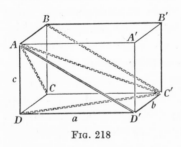

FIG. 218

a cut through $ABC'D'$ and obtain two wedges. Take the wedge $ABCDC'D'$ and cut it down the plane ADC', obtaining a triangular pyramid $ADD'C'$ and a rectangular one $ABCDC'$. Finally, bisect the rectangular pyramid by a cut in the plane ACC', obtaining two more triangular pyramids $ABCC'$, $ADCC'$.

Then pyramid $ABCC'$ = pyramid $ADCC'$ in volume, having the same height CC' and congruent bases ABC, ADC. Also pyramid $ADCC'$ = pyramid $ADD'C'$ in volume, having the same height AD and congruent bases DCC', $DD'C'$. Hence all three pyramids are equal in volume, and each is one-sixth the volume of the cuboid $= \frac{1}{6}abc = \frac{1}{3}(\frac{1}{2}ab)c = \frac{1}{3}$ base area × height.

If the model is made of wood it will be necessary to plane the faces down again after the saw-cuts have been made and smoothed, otherwise it will not fit to form a cuboid after the planing. It is of course unnecessary to dissect the second wedge.

4.2.2. A sectioned cone. It is often desirable to have a

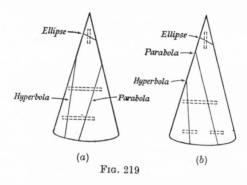

(a)   (b)

Fig. 219

model showing the sections of a circular cone. The construction involves some accurate work on a lathe. After the cone is roughly turned down the saw-cuts can be made and planed smooth. The cone is then dowelled together again and of course no longer fits. The whole must now be remounted in the lathe, preferably secured by wrapping round with string or binding, and the cone turned down again and finished off.

There are two ways of showing the sections; that of Fig. 219 (a) is the easier to make; the other is perhaps preferable mathematically.

4.2.3. Torus, showing seven-colour map. The famous

four-colour problem continues to interest and to baffle mathematicians. The fact that the problem is completely solved on the torus, seven colours being both necessary and sufficient, is surprising enough to provide interest in a model of the seven-colour map. The usual way in which the map is depicted is by means of the rectangle with opposite edges identified, which is equivalent to the torus, and can be imagined deformed into one without much difficulty. The map is shown below in this form; it consists of seven hexagons, each of which touches the other six.

If it is practicable to turn a torus on the lathe, the map itself can be marked out and coloured. Divide the 'waist' of the torus into three by three points. Then describe a helical curve

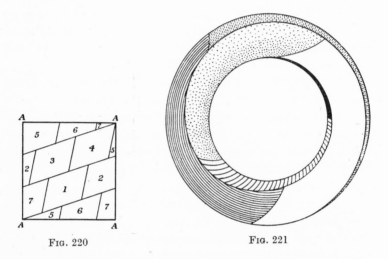

FIG. 220   FIG. 221

on the torus which begins at one point, travels all round the torus and returns to the next point, and so on until after three circuits the curve returns to its starting-point. Divide the whole length of this curve into fourteen equal parts. Then join the first point of subdivision to the sixth, the third to the eighth, the fifth to the tenth, and so on until every even point $2n$ is joined to the odd point $2n-5$. The result will be seven elongated areas, each in contact with the remaining six.

4.2.4. Plane section of torus. It is also interesting to show the section of a torus by a tangent plane through its centre. Such a plane will touch the surface at two diametrically opposite points, above and below the plane of symmetry. The section, surprisingly, consists of two circles intersecting at the points of contact. A model can be made of wood.

4.3. QUADRIC SURFACES

These are surfaces whose Cartesian equations are of the second degree and are analogous to the ellipse, parabola, and hyperbola in plane geometry. An equation of the second degree in the plane yields, apart from the case of an isolated point, either two straight lines, a circle, an ellipse, parabola, or hyperbola. In space the possibilities are more numerous, and include two planes, circular, elliptic, parabolic, and hyperbolic cylinders and cones, the sphere, spheroid and ellipsoid, two different hyperboloids, and the elliptic and hyperbolic paraboloids. We shall describe models of most of these.

4.3.1. Cylinders. These are made with the greatest of ease from an ordinary sheet of paper or card, rolled into a cylinder of circular, elliptic, or hyperbolic cross-section. The circular cylinder itself arises in multifarious examples from everyday life.

Nevertheless it has interesting properties, among which the following can be demonstrated with a model.

(a) An oblique plane section is an ellipse, as can be seen by sawing the broomstick, or cutting oblique slices from the polony or cucumber.

(b) If a sheet of paper is wrapped several times round the broomstick before the saw-cut is made, the edge of the paper will be cut into a neat sine-curve: an excellent way of manufacturing decorative shelf-paper.

(c) A straight line ruled obliquely on the paper will, when the paper is rolled into a circular cylinder, be transformed into a helix—the 'screw-thread' curve.

(d) By using an ordinary compass on a cylindrical surface, an oval curve can be drawn, but it is not an exact ellipse.

4.3.2. Cones. These again are 'developable' surfaces—i.e. they can be unrolled into a plane, and can be produced by bending sheets of paper or card. The circular cone is made from the sector of a circle. This is seen in the common filter-funnel, and some lamp-shades. These latter are more often in the form of a frustum of a cone, which unrolls into a sector of the ring between two concentric circles. In this case a second cone can be described containing the two bounding circles of the lampshade, with its vertex lying between them (see Fig. 222). If now a lamp is placed exactly at this vertex, the shadow of the shade cast by the lamp on a plane surface, such as a wall or ceiling, will be a conic section. In the normal vertical position hyperbolas will appear on the walls and a circle on the

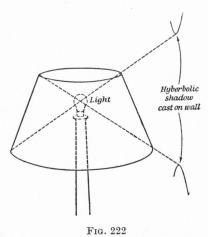

FIG. 222

floor or ceiling. By tilting the lamp the ellipse and parabola can be produced. Many lamps are sufficiently near this configuration to show the sections quite well.

A wooden cone cut to show the sections has been described in 4.2.2 above.

The circular sector rolled up to form a cone demonstrates

(a) that the radius of the sector is the slant height of the cone;

(b) that the arc of the sector is the circumference of the base of the cone;

(c) that the area of the curved surface of the cone is $\frac{1}{2}$ base-circumference × slant height.

By drawing straight lines on the flat sector geodesics on the cone can be shown; in particular it appears that the shortest route from a point on the base-circle round the cone and back to itself is not the circumference of this circle.

4.3.3. Sphere. Spheres confront us everywhere from the days of the rubber ball in the nursery to those of the globe in the geography room. Nevertheless, the geometry on their surface is not always easy to visualize, and the geographer often has the advantage of the mathematician in having a globe with meridians and parallels drawn on it ready to hand. On such a solid globe great circles can be drawn and measured, and their geodetic property is more apparent. The following is a method of constructing a skeleton 'armillary' sphere made of great

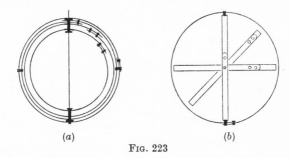

(a)   (b)

Fig. 223

circles only, by means of which latitude and longitude (polar angles) and the properties of the general spherical triangle can be studied. (The description is taken from the American *18th Yearbook*, p. 242.) The sphere can be made very conveniently from steel strapping of the kind which is fitted round packing-cases. This is easily cut and punched or drilled, and can be fastened with brass stationers' or shoemakers' eyelets. A complete model so made appears in Plate 4c.

We begin by making a circle of strapping with two holes in it at opposite ends of a diameter. This must be done accurately, as the rest of the work depends on it. Cut a strip 1 inch longer than the circumference required; mark a point about ½ inch from the centre and punch a hole there. Mark off equal lengths equal to half the circumference from this hole and punch two more holes. Coil the strip round and join these holes temporarily with an eyelet. In the overlap, punch a hole right through and secure it. Next place two other circles inside this one; they should be coiled to fit inside before joining up with two eyelets apiece. The joins are then staggered round the circumference and holes are drilled through the set of rings using the outer holes as a guide. The three are then fixed together with two eyelets. Finally, an outer equatorial ring is fixed to the outermost of the three by two eyelets at the ends of the diameter at right angles to that on which the other three pivot. We then have a skeleton sphere consisting of the equator and three variable meridians at right angles to it. The equator itself can

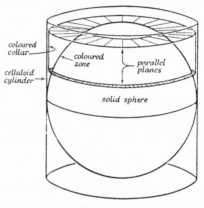

coloured collar

coloured zone

parallel planes

celluloid cylinder

solid sphere

FIG. 224

be rotated if necessary to give a spherical triangle of any shape.

The whole frame can be conveniently mounted on a bill-file, passing through the two pivotal eyelets.

4.3.4. Sphere and cylinder—Archimedes' theorem. Another useful demonstration model in connexion with the sphere is one constructed to show the fundamental theorem of Archimedes on which the mensuration of the sphere depends. This result, which the great Greek mathematician considered one of his greatest discoveries, states the equality of the areas intercepted by two parallel planes on the sphere and a cylinder circumscribing it with axis perpendicular to the planes.

Any solid ball will do for the sphere—a large nursery ball is a reasonable size. The cylinder can be made of thin celluloid sheet joined with a celluloid solvent—acetone, nail-polish remover, or durofix. Two flat circular sheets of celluloid or

'Perspex', of the diameter of the sphere, serve for the planes, with concentric circles of different sizes cut out of them.

It is a good plan to fit a thin collar of coloured transparent sheet between them, inside the transparent cylinder, to which it can be cemented. This serves both to space the cutting planes and also to delineate the area on the cylinder which is under consideration. The equal area on the sphere can be painted to match.

4.3.5. The general quadrics constructed from circular sections. The next most general quadric after the sphere is the quadric of revolution; either the spheroids, or the paraboloid, or the two hyperboloids of revolution of one and two sheets respectively. These can of course be turned on a lathe in wood (given the necessary skill, and a template shaped to the curve of section by a plane through the axis). Spheroids of both kinds are familiar wherever oranges and plums are eaten or rugby football is played; the hyperboloid of one sheet can sometimes be seen in the form of a waste-paper basket, or in the attempt to turn a cylinder on a lathe when the tool has travelled in a line which is not parallel to the axis.

The paraboloid appears when a cylinder of liquid is rotated at speed—a dangerous experiment in inexperienced hands! The hyperboloid of two sheets is not a common form of surface and there seems no everyday example of it.

But it is more interesting to make the general quadrics with an elliptic central section. If they are constructed in the following way, from their circular sections, it is not difficult.

4.3.6. The ellipsoid constructed from its circular sections. A description of this model is given in *Analytical Geometry of Three Dimensions*, by W. H. McCrea, p. 110. Since the model is deformable, there is no need to begin by drawing the ellipse as there suggested, since in one position it will be spherical.

Begin then by drawing a circle as shown in Fig. 225 (*a*). Mark two perpendicular diameters, and on each of them a number of equally spaced points, symmetrically placed with respect to the centre. If the model is to take up naturally the form of an ellipsoid, the numbers on the two diameters should be unequal. Chords are now obtained by joining up the points in corresponding pairs, giving two sets of parallel chords. Avoid divisions in which the resulting chords have points of intersection very near their ends.

Now cut out from thin card a set of circles with diameter equal in length to each one of these chords. Mark off along each diameter points corresponding to the points of intersec-

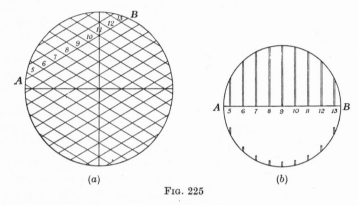

(a)   (b)

FIG. 225

tion of this chord with members of the other set. It is as well to number these points to correspond with the chords. When this has been done, cut slots through each of these points perpendicular to the diameter: above the diameter for chords of one set, and below it for chords of the other. The circle corresponding to chord AB is shown. The slots should be wide enough to take the thickness of the card.

The circular disks are then fitted together on the 'egg-box' principle, corresponding slots being slid together in opposite directions.

The resulting model can be fixed together either by sticking strips of 'Sellotape' down the 'hinges', or by fixing links across the ends of each slot and cutting small nicks (shown dotted in Fig. 225 (b)) to accommodate them.

The model is collapsible; it can be flattened out into a plane ellipse in both directions, and takes up various shapes of ellipsoid on the way; one axis remains constant and the other two vary continuously in such a way that $a^2\cos^2\theta + b^2\sin^2\theta$ remains constant, where 2θ is the angle between the diameters in Fig. 225 (a). For a photograph of the finished model, see Plate 3 a.

The two hyperboloids and the elliptic paraboloid can be made in the same way. In these cases the hyperbola or parabola must first be drawn and symmetrically placed sets of parallel

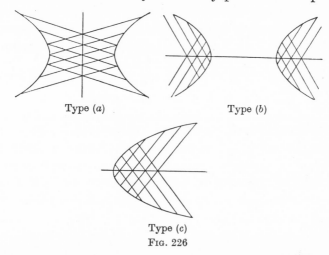

Type (a)   Type (b)

Type (c)
FIG. 226

chords inserted as in the diagrams. The rest of the construction then proceeds as before.

The hyperbolic paraboloid has no circular sections, but it can be constructed as a ruled surface (see below).

These models can be painted in four colours, one on each set of parallel faces of each set of circles. The colour change on deformation of the model is quite startling—indeed the whole thing is reminiscent of the nursery jack-in-the-box!

4.4. RULED SURFACES

Ruled surfaces are obvious subjects for models, and are suitable for treatment in various materials. Cardboard and coloured thread makes a model which can be folded and carried about in the pocket. Plywood and thread is more durable and can be strutted to remain rigid. 'Perspex' has the advantage of transparency, so that the surface can be viewed from any angle. Polyvinylchloride (PVC plastic) thread is excellent for the pur-

pose if a stout model is required. It is smooth and collects no
dust, is self-coloured, and slightly elastic. If the model is to
be made deformable, elastic thread (coloured Shirlastic) must
be used, as PVC changes shape too slowly. The only trouble
with PVC is that as the plasticizer evaporates the thread is
apt to become brittle, and re-threading may be necessary; this
is not usually an arduous task. Finally, the lines can be made

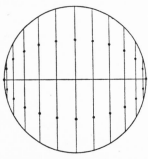

of wire or fine brass rod. At least
one hyperboloid exists with wire
generators, each of which is jointed
to each generator that meets it by
universal joints, so that the whole
is collapsible both into an ellipse and
a hyperbola. This calls for super-
lative craftsmanship of an order
not usually encountered in schools.

FIG. 227. Construction of
ellipse.

The planes between which the
thread is stretched to form the
surface need to be held apart by rigid struts. A suitable
method is to make use of plastic tubing, which can often be
obtained in the form of paint-brush handles at the chain stores.
A knitting-needle or other rod is passed down the tube, and
the planes are secured to the ends by nuts which the needle
is threaded to receive. (It is wise to soften knitting-needles by
heating before attempting to cut a thread on them.) These
tubes are easily cut to lengths with a sharp knife, and can be
obtained in different colours. A highly pleasing model can easily
be made in this way, and for a very modest expenditure. As an
alternative, dowel rod can be used. The construction of several
types of ruled surface will now be described. Models of a
number of them, made of 'Perspex', appear in Plate 3, b and c.

4.4.1. Hyperboloid of one sheet. Draw a circle on a sheet
of paper and divide its circumference into twenty-four or
thirty-six equal parts, starting from the end of a given diameter.
Draw ordinates from all the points to this diameter and reduce
them in a fixed ratio, say by one-half, thus obtaining a set of
points on an ellipse whose eccentric angles have a constant

difference (Fig. 227). With this as a template mark the points in exact correspondence on two rectangular 'Perspex' or ply-wood sheets, and also mark four points in the corners for

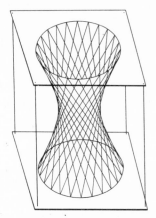

FIG. 228. Completed hyperboloid.

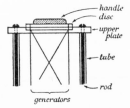
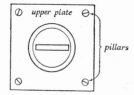

FIG. 229

the struts. Drill all holes with the sheets clamped together. (Before drilling 'Perspex', press a heated needle on the points to be drilled, to stop the drill wandering.) Then set up the two planes on the struts and secure. Begin threading from the end of a diameter on one plane to a hole about 120° further round on the other (to obtain a good 'waist'). Continue round in the same direction, progressing one hole top and bottom each time. Then with a different coloured thread join up the other set of generators, joining the first point to the point 120° in the opposite direction, and so on. The resulting surface is shown in the figure.

If the ends are made circular instead of elliptic, a hyperboloid of revolution is obtained. It is possible in this case to mount the upper circle of holes on a disk which can be rotated relative to the bottom. If this is done, as the disk rotates, one set of generators will open out towards a cylinder, the other set will close in towards a cone. If we join each point of the lower circle to the point 90° in front of it for one set of generators, and then for the other set join each point to the point 90° behind it, taking care that the second set of generators lies wholly outside the first set, then a rotation of the upper circle through 90° will bring the inner set of generators into the form of a cone and the outer set into that of a circular cylinder. Intermediate rotations give various forms of hyperboloid. Since in this rotation the length of the generators alters, they must be made of elastic thread. This is a fascinating model if a little trouble is taken to get it accurately and smoothly made. A possible method of making the disk is shown in Fig. 229.

An alternative way of making an adjustable hyperboloid has been suggested by R. F. Wheeler. In this, both sets of generators of the hyperboloid are continuously deformable from a cylinder to a cone. The method of construction should be clear from the accompanying diagram (Fig. 230); 'Perspex' can be used throughout, the disks and annuli being made of sheet, and the handles of rod.

4.4.2. Hyperbolic paraboloid. A model of a part of this surface can be very simply made. Take two sheets of card or 'Perspex', and mark on them two equal isosceles triangles with their bases along an edge of each sheet. Mount the sheets edge to edge so that these bases coincide. If card is used a hinge of linen or cellulose tape can be used; 'Perspex' can be mitred and cemented or hinged with small brass hinges. Drill holes at equal intervals down the sides of the two triangles and thread them so that if the triangles were opened out flat a network of parallel lines would be formed as shown (Fig. 231 (a)).

If it is desired to make the model so that it actually can be opened flat, the thread must be elastic. Otherwise an angle of about 90° between the planes is desirable. There is a model of

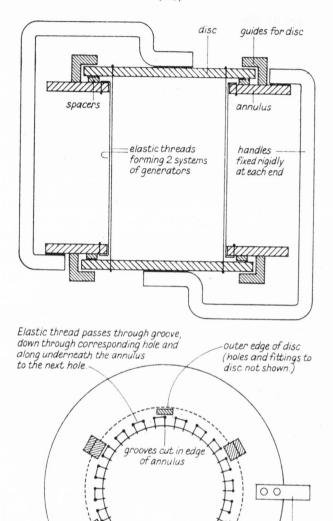

disc   guides for disc

spacers

annulus

elastic threads
forming 2 systems
of generators

handles
fixed rigidly
at each end

Elastic thread passes through groove,
down through corresponding hole and
along underneath the annulus
to the next hole.

outer edge of disc
(holes and fittings to
disc not shown.)

grooves cut in edge
of annulus

handle
fastened
to annulus

spacers

guides for disc

Fig. 230

this type in the Science Museum which has brass strips for the sides of the triangles. These are hinged together so that the lower one rests in a horizontal plane. This one is perforated so that the threads attached to the upper movable triangle pass

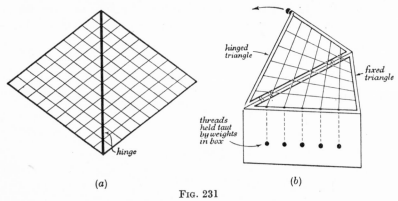

hinged triangle

fixed triangle

threads held taut by weights in box

hinge

(a)   (b)

FIG. 231

through it and are held taut by small weights concealed in a prism-shaped box (Fig. 231 (b)). The shape of the paraboloid can thus be varied from the plane parabola, when the triangles are in coincidence, to the flat rhombus, when the angle between them is 180°.

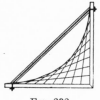

FIG. 232

If the model is made at a fixed angle, a strut should be fitted for rigidity between the apices of the triangles, as in the end-on view shown (Fig. 232 and Plate 3 b, No. 1).

A second method of constructing a model of the hyperbolic paraboloid is described by McCrea (*Analytical Geometry of Three Dimensions*, p. 123). Whereas the previous model shows the intersection of tangent planes with the surface—the four generators which form the boundary of the model—this gives a clearer picture of the parabolas in which the surface is met by planes parallel to its principal planes.

We begin by drawing a rectangle and its two diagonals, to represent the generators through the vertex. On each side of the rectangle erect symmetrical parabolic arcs of equal height, as shown in Fig. 233. One opposite pair of these will be bent upwards, at right angles to the plane of the rectangle $ABCD$; the other pair downwards.

To locate the holes for threading, divide each diagonal AC, BD into an equal number of equal parts. Draw through each point of division parallels to the other diagonal, to meet the sides. At the points of intersection, erect ordinates to the

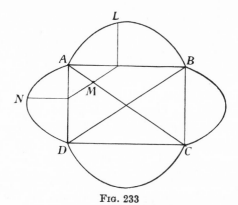

FIG. 233

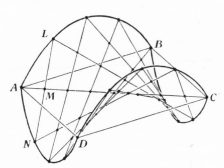

FIG. 234

parabolic arcs. These meet the arcs at the ends of a generator. For example, in Fig. 233, the three points L, M, N will lie on a single generator. Fig. 234 shows the finished surface.

If this model is made in 'Perspex', it will be difficult to drill the holes at the correct angles through the sheet $ABCD$ along the diagonals. It will be better therefore to mark the four parabolas in position on the side faces of an open box; a lid can be cemented in, if desired, after threading, to enclose and protect the whole model (Plate 3 b, No. 3).

4.4.3. The twisted cubic. Two quadric surfaces will in general intersect in a curve of degree 4. But if they have a generator in common (which means that in real geometry they must be *ruled* surfaces) then the curve of intersection will consist of this generator and a curve of degree 3, called a *twisted*, or *space cubic*. It can be proved that this cubic is not a plane curve, that it meets the common generator in two points, that infinitely many quadric surfaces can be drawn to contain it, and that in particular the chords through any point of it generate a quadric cone. A model to show some of these facts is well worth constructing and throws a flood of light on the relationships of the various surfaces. The mathematics is interesting in itself.

We shall describe a special case, when the twisted cubic touches the common generator at infinity. Further, for simplicity we shall take the quadrics to be a hyperboloid of revolution and a cylinder whose sections by planes perpendicular to the axis of the hyperboloid are circles. It will be found that the sections of the quadric cones by the same planes are also circles.

Consider the hyperboloid $(x^2+y^2)/a^2 - z^2/c^2 = 1$. Take the intersection of $x = a$ and $cy = az$ as common generator. The plane $cy = az$ touches the hyperboloid at infinity; the plane $x = a$ touches it on its 'waist' in the plane $z = 0$, which is the circle $x^2+y^2 = a^2$ in that plane. The cylinder which contains this generator, touches $cy = az$, has circular sections by planes $z = $ constant, and contains the point $(0, a, 0)$ (a further simplification) is $(x/a-1)^2 + (y/a-z/c-1)^2 = 1$. Any point on this cylinder is given by the equations

$$\begin{cases} x = a(1-\sin\theta), \\ y = a(t+1-\cos\theta), \\ z = ct, \end{cases}$$

and will lie on the hyperboloid (and hence on the cubic, provided $\cos\theta \neq 1$) if $t+1 = \cot\frac{1}{2}\theta$. (The reader can verify this by substitution in the equation.)

The quadric cone which has vertex at $(0, a, 0)$ and includes the twisted cubic can be found by eliminating θ in such a way as to obtain a homogeneous equation in x, $y-a$, z; again the reader can verify that its equation is

$$c\{x^2+(y-a)^2\}+az(x-y+a) = 0.$$

Its section by the plane $z = ct$ is the circle

$$x(x+at)+(y-a)(y-a-at) = 0,$$

which has the join of $(0,a)$, $(-at, a+at)$ for diameter.

The situation in the plane $z = ct$ is shown in the diagram (Fig. 235). The geometry of it is interesting. The three circular sections of cone, hyperboloid, and cylinder are shown. P is the point on the twisted cubic, R the point on the common generator. The circle ABC is the orthogonal projection of the 'waist' of the hyperboloid: PQ that of the generator through P belonging to the opposite system to the common generator. The geometry of the figure shows the equality of the angles RKP, COQ, TLP, all of which are equal to θ. Hence, as P traces out the twisted cubic, the generators of the three quadrics rotate at equal rates about the circular sections. This fact makes construction of a model very easy. The figure will well repay careful study. RAR' is the projection of the common generator of cylinder and hyperboloid; TBT' that of the cylinder and cone; and SBS' that of the cone and hyperboloid.

To make the model, construct the diagram of Fig. 235 for two values of t; $t = +3$ and $t = -3$ are convenient. In the plane $z = 3c$ the circles are

Hyperboloid: $x^2+y^2 = 10a^2$

Cylinder: $(x-a)^2+(y-4a)^2 = a^2$

Cone: $\left(x+\dfrac{3a}{2}\right)^2+\left(y-\dfrac{5a}{2}\right)^2 = \dfrac{9a^2}{2}$

and the point P on the twisted cubic is $\left(\dfrac{9a}{17}, \dfrac{53a}{17}, 3c\right)$.

In the plane $z = -3c$ the circles are

Hyperboloid: $x^2+y^2 = 10a^2$

Cylinder: $(x-a)^2+(y+2a)^2 = a^2$

Cone: $\left(x-\dfrac{3a}{2}\right)^2+\left(y+\dfrac{a}{2}\right)^2 = \dfrac{9a^2}{2}$

and P is now $\left(\dfrac{9a}{5}, -\dfrac{13a}{5}, -3c\right)$. The diagram is drawn to scale for $t = 3$; the circles for $t = -3$ are shown pecked.

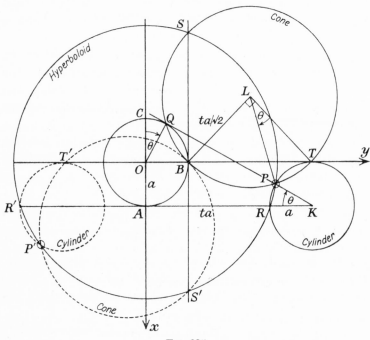

Fig. 235

Inscribe these circles on two sheets of 'Perspex'; drill holes at equal angular intervals round the circles. Since it will be convenient to pass both sets of generators of the hyperboloid through the same holes, we shall need a hole at R; in addition we need to accommodate the generators coming up from the opposite plane. The values of θ at $t = \pm 3$ are $28°\ 4'$ and $306°\ 52'$; if we take forty subdivisions we can approximate to these as $27°$ and $306°$ with sufficient accuracy. A large model will, however, be needed to include forty generators on the cylinder. We therefore mark off points on the three circles, starting from P in each of the planes, at angular intervals of $9°$. It will be found that in each case the drill-holes for the hyperboloid will fall at the points on the axes within the limits of error; the generators are threaded from each hole on one circle to the points sixteen holes away on the opposite circle. One generator of each system on the hyperboloid, cone, and cylinder will pass through each point of the twisted cubic, which can be marked by a bead threaded on the four generators. A completed model appears in Plate 3 d.

The twisted cubic can also be displayed in a model as the edge of regression of the surface formed by its tangents. The simplest method is to consider the cubic given by the parametric equations $x:y:z:a = \theta^3:\theta^2:\theta:1$. The equations for the tangent at θ are then $x-2\theta y+\theta^2 z = 0$ and $y-2\theta z+\theta^2 a = 0$. The surface can be conveniently generated by threads stretched between the planes of the cube $x = \pm a$, $y = \pm a$, $z = \pm a$. It will be found that the curves of section in the planes $x = \pm a$ are mirror images; in $x = +a$ they are given by

$$\frac{y}{a} = \frac{\theta^3+2}{3\theta}; \qquad \frac{z}{a} = \frac{1+2\theta^3}{3\theta^2}.$$

In the same way the curves in $z = \pm a$ are mirror images; that in $z = a$ is given by $x/a = 3\theta^2-2\theta^3$, $y/a = 2\theta-\theta^2$. In the plane $y = a$, however, there are no intersections within the cube-face; in $y = -a$ we have $z = \frac{1}{2}\left(\theta-\frac{1}{\theta}\right)$, $x = -\frac{\theta}{2}(3+\theta^2)$. The cube is conveniently made in the form of an open box of 'Perspex' with the plane $y = a$ missing; the points on the other planes should be plotted by giving values to θ from $-1\cdot6$ to $+1\cdot6$. If this is done at intervals of $0\cdot1$ it will be found that only two points (for $\theta = \pm0\cdot5$) fall on $y = -a$. The points are drilled and the surface threaded as usual. The resulting model is shown in Fig. 236. The open plane $y = a$ is at the top; $z = a$ is at the front left, $x = a$ at the front right.

4.4.4. Quartic with two double-lines. As an example of ruled surfaces of higher degree we select first the quartic surface with two perpendicular double-lines whose central section is a circle. This is a surface of great importance in optics, for it is the envelope traced out by the rays of a pencil reflected or refracted at a spherical surface. These rays pass through two

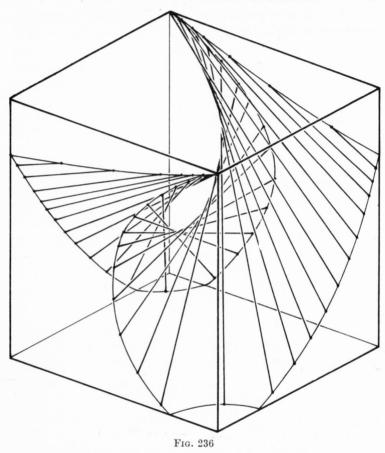

Fig. 236

focal lines at right angles, midway between which is the 'circle of least confusion', the minimum section of the quartic surface formed by the rays. A simple but not very convincing example of such a surface is provided by the 'old-fashioned humbug'. These potent sweetmeats seem to be made by twisting the material in just this way between two perpendicular skew lines at their extremities. A long foolscap envelope, with its open end sealed in a line perpendicular to its closed end, has also approximately this shape.

To construct a model, take two square plates of 'Perspex' or plywood and mark on them two congruent ellipses with their

major axis three times the minor axis. Points are marked out
on the circumference of the ellipses separated by constant
differences in eccentric angle. Holes for the threads are drilled
at these points. (It is simplest to mark only one ellipse in fact,
and to drill right through the two sheets clamped together.)

Fig. 237 shows how to construct the points and also how to
join up the points in the subsequent threading.

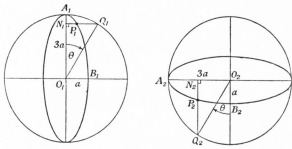

Fɪɢ. 237

$P_1 N_1 = \frac{1}{3} Q_1 N_1$, $P_2 N_2 = \frac{1}{3} Q_2 N_2$, $A_1 \hat{O}_1 Q_1 = B_2 \hat{O}_2 Q_2$ and is in
the same sense. The ellipses are mounted in parallel planes
with their major axes at right angles. A point such as P_1 with
eccentric angle θ on the upper ellipse is joined by a thread to
the point P_2 with eccentric angle $\frac{1}{2}\pi + \theta$ on the lower ellipse,
the radii $O_1 Q_1$, $O_2 Q_2$ being always directed in diametrically
opposite directions.

If the ellipses have semi-axes $3a$, a and are in planes $4b$ apart,
we can take the axes of x and y parallel to the major and minor
axis of one ellipse, and the axis of z as the line joining their
centres, the origin being the mid-point of this line. Then the
five points

$$(3a \cos \theta, a \sin \theta, 2b), \quad (2a \cos \theta, 0, b), \quad (a \cos \theta, -a \sin \theta, 0),$$

$$(0, -2a \sin \theta, -b), \quad (-a \cos \theta, -3a \sin \theta, -2b),$$

are always collinear, so that the generators of the surface intersect the lines $(y = 0, z = b)$, $(x = 0, z = -b)$, in a segment of
length $2a$, and also the circle $x^2 + y^2 = a^2$, $z = 0$.

The exact value of the ratio b/a is immaterial but it is convenient to have it about $2:1$ or $3:2$. The positions of the coordinate axes, double lines, and central circle are shown in Fig. 238. A model is shown in Plate $3c$.

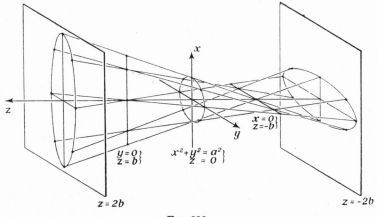

FIG. 238

4.4.5. Right helicoid.

As a further example of ruled surfaces the right helicoid will be briefly discussed. This is the surface swept out by a line which always intersects a fixed axis at right angles and which rotates uniformly as its point of intersection moves uniformly along the axis. It intersects any cylinder concentric with the axis in a helix—the screw-thread curve. Small aerials in the form of a right helicoid are familiar to wireless enthusiasts.

A model of the surface is easily made from wire, soldered at right angles to a rigid rod for axis. A more interesting model is obtained with rather more trouble by threading between curves in perpendicular planes.

If we take the axis of z along the axis of the helicoid, its equation can be taken as $y = x \tan(z/a)$. We wish to find the curves in which this surface is met by two planes through Ox, bisecting the angles between the planes xOz and xOy. The easiest way to do this is to take these as coordinate planes, by rotating the axes of y and z through $\frac{1}{4}\pi$ and leaving the axis of x unaltered. Then if y' and z' are new coordinates,

$$y = \frac{y'-z'}{\sqrt{2}}, \qquad z = \frac{y'+z'}{\sqrt{2}},$$

so that the equation of the surface becomes

$$y'-z' = x\sqrt{2}\tan\frac{y'+z'}{a\sqrt{2}}.$$

Dropping the dashes, we obtain for the curves of section with the planes $y = 0$ and $z = 0$,

$$\begin{cases} y = 0 \\ \dfrac{x}{a} = -\dfrac{z}{a\sqrt{2}}\cot\left(\dfrac{z}{a\sqrt{2}}\right) \end{cases} \text{ and } \begin{cases} z = 0 \\ \dfrac{x}{a} = \dfrac{y}{a\sqrt{2}}\cot\left(\dfrac{y}{a\sqrt{2}}\right). \end{cases}$$

The curves are identical, but face in opposite directions.

The whole of the line $y = 0$, $z = 0$ lies in the surface, but on the first plane $y = 0$, $x \to -a$ as $z \to 0$, whereas on $z = 0$, $x \to +a$ as $y \to 0$.

If $a = 100$, corresponding values of x and y for the curve of section with $z = 0$ are given in the accompanying table at equal intervals of y.

y	0	18·5	37	55·5	74	92·5	111	129·5	148	166·5
x	100	99·5	97·7	95·1	90·7	85·3	78·5	70·3	60·4	48·9

y	185	203·5	222	240·5	259	277·5	296	314·5	333	351·5
x	35·1	19·0	0	−22·4	−49·0	−81·1	−120·6	−170·3	−235	−323

These points are now plotted on two plates and drilled through. The plates are then mounted at right angles, after being bevelled along the x-axis, so that they lie, with their x-axes coincident, in the planes $y = 0, z = 0$. Care must be taken to ensure that the origin coincides. It is convenient to drill an extra hole at the origin so that a thread can be stretched from it to a strut between the plates, lying along the axis of the helicoid.

The generators are threaded between the drill-holes corresponding to points with equal values of y and z. The resulting surface is shown in Fig. 239.

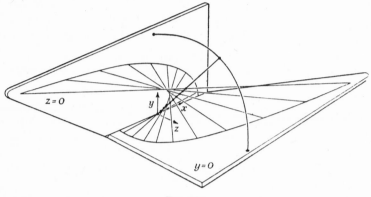

FIG. 239

4.4.6. Other ruled surfaces. There are of course a large number of other surfaces which can be made. Some of the most interesting ones are the 'twist surfaces' allied to the Möbius strip, which is discussed more fully in the section that follows.

Imagine a point P moving round a fixed circle. If the point carries a line l which is always perpendicular to the tangent to the circle at P, the motion of l will generate a ruled surface.

(i) If l is perpendicular to the plane of the circle, it will generate a circular cylinder.

(ii) If l passes through a fixed point it will generate a circular cone.

(iii) If l rotates about the tangent as axis with half the angular velocity with which P describes the circle, l describes the 'half-twist' surface. This is of the same kind—except that it extends to infinity—as the surface of a strip of paper twisted once (a half-revolution) and joined end to end—the Möbius strip of the first order. The surface is therefore one-sided. It has the cubic equation

$$(x^2+y^2+z^2)y-2z(x^2+y^2)-2azx-a^2y = 0$$

(the circle being $x^2+y^2 = a^2$, $z = 0$; and the initial position of l, $x = -a$, $y = 0$).

There is a line of double-points, $x = -a$, $y = z$, and the axis of z lies wholly on the surface.

The surface is conveniently made by joining points on the curves in which it is cut by planes $z = \pm\lambda a$. These points can be plotted parametrically by observing that the generators are the lines joining $(a\cos\theta, a\sin\theta, 0)$ to $(0, 0, -a\tan\frac{1}{2}\theta)$. See Plate 3 c.

A model could of course be made with rather less trouble in wire.

(iv) If l rotates about the tangent with the same angular velocity as P, it describes the 'full-twist' surface, equivalent to the Möbius strip of the second order. This is a quartic surface with equation

$$y^4 + x^2(y^2 - z^2) - 2axyz - a^2y^2 = 0.$$

It is two-sided, and it has the x-axis and the z-axis as double-lines. The 'one-and-a-half-twist' surface, corresponding to the Möbius strip of the third order, is again one-sided, of a more complicated shape. Higher order twist surfaces can be similarly defined. See A. Emch, *Mathematical Models*, Univ. Illinois Bulletin, **18** (1920) 12.

4.5. Möbius Strips

Take a long strip of paper with parallel edges. If the ends are brought together and joined, a cylindrical surface is formed with two sides and two bounding edges. But if one edge of the original strip is turned through 180° before joining, the resulting surface has only one side and only one bounding edge (Fig. 240). It is usually called a *Möbius strip* after the geometer who first discovered its properties. Any point on the strip can be joined to any other point on the strip by a curve lying wholly on the strip and not crossing the bounding edge. This is not the case with the ordinary two-sided surface.

The bounding edge is not knotted, and can be deformed into a circle, carrying the surface with it, which must be allowed to intersect itself. If this is done the resulting surface is known as a *cross-cap*. Of course it is still one-sided. Such a cross-cap is shown in perspective and in a contoured plan in Figs. 241 (a) and (b).

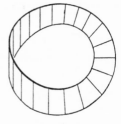

FIG. 240

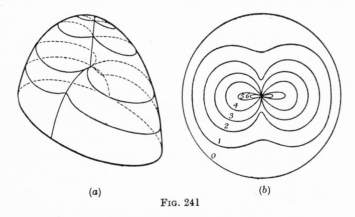

(a)   (b)

FIG. 241

If the strip is twisted through 360° before joining, a 'Möbius strip of the second order' results. It is two-sided and has two boundary curves, but they are linked together. Generally, if there are n half-twists before joining, we obtain the Möbius strip of the nth order. If n is odd, the surface is one-sided and possesses a single boundary curve which is knotted for $n \geqslant 3$; if n is even it has two sides and two linked boundaries.

Some amusement can be had by cutting Möbius strips of various orders down their centre-lines. If n is even, two strips similar to the original result, linked together in the same way as the boundary curves. If n is odd, only one strip results, similar to the boundary curve, i.e. for $n \geqslant 3$ it is knotted. It has $2n+2$ half-twists: n for each circuit of the original and two extra gained when the coils are opened out. If the strips are trisected, the centre strip will resemble the original, but the outer strips will be single or a pair, like the result of bisection, and they will be linked to the centre ring.

4.6. ONE-SIDED SURFACES AND THE KLEIN BOTTLE

A *closed* surface with only one side seems at first sight to be impossible, but it is easily obtained in the following way. Take a piece of rubber tubing—an old piece of cycle inner-tube will do—and turn one end outside in, like a 'flyped' sock, or a non-spill ink-well. Push this down inside the tube and bring it out through a slit in the side. Then take it round and join it on (still inside-out) to the other end of the tube. The result is the *Klein bottle*, which has only one side, and no boundary. It can also be obtained (in imagination) by uniting the parallel edges of a first-order Möbius strip to form a closed tube, which necessitates allowing the tube to intersect itself in the above manner. It is deformable into a sphere with two small circles removed and replaced by two cross-caps, but most people find this far from obvious and very difficult to visualize. An algebraic surface with this form has equation

$$a^2(x^2+y^2)(b^2-x^2-y^2) = z^2(a^2x^2+b^2y^2).$$

A beautiful Klein bottle of blown glass was exhibited by Professor Hassé at the Mathematical Association's Visual Aids Exhibition in 1947. A diagram of the Klein bottle is shown in Fig. 242 (*a*). With it (Fig. 242 (*b*)) is given a diagram of another famous one-sided surface—the quartic surface

$$y^2z^2+z^2x^2+x^2y^2+xyz = 0.$$

This surface was investigated by Steiner who called it the 'Roman surface', but in this country it is more commonly known by the name of its discoverer. It contains each axis as a double-line, and has 'pinch-points' at $(\pm\frac{1}{2}, 0, 0)$, $(0, \pm\frac{1}{2}, 0)$, $(0, 0, \pm\frac{1}{2})$. Further, it touches the plane $x+y+z = \frac{1}{2}$ along the circle through the pinch-points lying in this plane, and contains three other similar circles in alternate octants. A model can be made of plasticine: it is well to begin with a fixed framework of three mutually perpendicular axes.

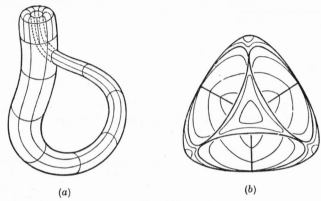

(a)

(b)

Fig. 242

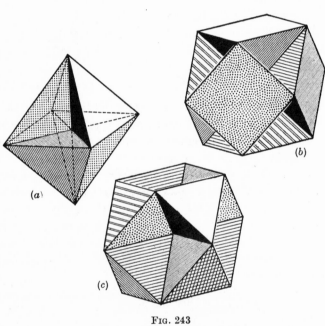

(a)

(b)

(c)

Fig. 243

(See p. 143)

4.6.1. This surface is homomorphic with (i.e. it can be continuously deformed into) a polyhedron consisting of alternate triangles of an octahedron joined by the three diametral squares. This obviously has the same symmetry and one-sidedness as the Steiner surface and is much easier to construct. A diagram of this polyhedron (the *heptahedron*) is given in Fig. 243 (*a*). Its net can be easily drawn if the trihedral 'dimples' are thought of as three separate triangular faces. The one-sidedness is most apparent if the surface is made of transparent material—cellophane or thin celluloid sheet. The heptahedron is an 'Archimedean' polyhedron in the broad sense, since all its faces are regular polygons and all its vertices are congruent. There are several other Archimedean polyhedra with diametral planes: the one depicted in Fig. 243 (*b*) is also one-sided; it has the squares and diametral hexagons of a cuboctahedron. Fig. 243 (*c*) shows the polyhedron referred to in 3.11 (2). It can be regarded as a 'deltahedron', or as consisting of the triangles and diametral hexagons of a cuboctahedron. It is two-sided, but the 'sides' meet at vertices, alternate triangles belonging to alternate 'sides'. In the case of the icosidodecahedron, either the triangular or the pentagonal faces may be removed and replaced by the diametral decagons; in either case a one-sided surface results of the same type as the first two depicted in the figure.

4.7. SPHERE-PACKS

This is a large subject and difficult to visualize without models. The general sphere-pack borders on the subject of crystallography and is rather more than elementary, but it is worth while studying the two types of close-packing, because everyone has some experience of packing spheres—tennis-balls, golf-balls, oranges, or even marbles!

The best, cheapest, and most uniform spheres for demonstration purposes are table-tennis balls. They can be stuck together with 'Durofix', or their waywardness can be overcome by confining them in a box or tray. This can be rectangular in shape to demonstrate cubic close-packing (face-centred cubic lattice). A square of sixteen balls will be needed as base if it is desired to show the twelve neighbours of a given ball. The arrangement of the balls in three layers 1, 2, 3, and the base of a unit cube of the face-centred lattice are shown in Fig. 244 (*a*).

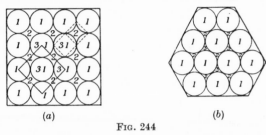

(*a*)   (*b*)

FIG. 244

Alternatively, both cubic and hexagonal close-packing can be demonstrated with a hexagonal base-layer of twelve balls, packed 2–3–4–3 as in Fig. 244 (*b*). For hexagonal close-packing the third layer of balls stands vertically over the first; for cubic it takes the position indicated and the fourth layer repeats the first. It is interesting to identify the two models of cubic close-packing; though unless a larger number of balls is used the complete face-centred cube does not appear in either model. The hexagonal tray necessary to enclose the second pile of balls has alternate sides $1+1/\sqrt{3} = 1{\cdot}577$ and $2+1/\sqrt{3} = 2{\cdot}577$ times the diameter of a ball. Instructions for making a cover for the stack are given by Hope-Jones, 'The Rhombic Dodecahedron for the Young', *Math. Gazette*, **20** (1936), 254, to which article the writers are considerably indebted. This article also discusses the connexion with the bee's cell, for which see also D'Arcy Thompson, *On Growth and Form*, pp. 525–44.

The rhombic dodecahedron arises in the cubic case if we imagine each ball swelled out to meet each of its twelve neighbours along the tangent plane; the area of contact becomes a rhombus, and the solids themselves are now rhombic dodecahedra.

In the case of the hexagonal close-pack the corresponding faces are rhombic, where a ball in layer 2 meets its three neighbours in each of layers 1 and 3, and trapezia, where it meets the six neighbours in its own layer. The ball thus becomes a twelve-sided solid called a *trapezo-rhombic dodecahedron* (Fig. 245).

The cubic and hexagonal close-packings are equally dense—i.e. an equal number of spheres can be packed by either method into a volume sufficiently large for edge effects to be neglected. This is obvious from the second model, where the two are seen to differ only by the arrangement of spheres in the layers, both the number of layers and the number of spheres in them being the same. The fraction of volume occupied is the ratio of the volume of a sphere to that of a rhombic dodecahedron, i.e. to two cubes of sides $r\sqrt{2}$, i.e. $\pi/3\sqrt{2}$. These cubes can be seen in the first model; the bases of two are shown in plan in broken lines in Fig. 244 (a). They are exactly the height of a layer, and their centres are alternately occupied and unoccupied by the centres of spheres. Each sphere therefore requires two cubes. The rhombic dodecahedron is formed by adding to the faces of one cube six square pyramids whose vertices are at centres of the neighbouring six (empty) cubes. These six pyramids exactly fit together to form one such cube. Hence again the volume of the rhombic dodecahedron is that of two such cubes.

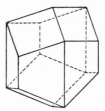

Fig. 245

The hexagons whose vertices are the centres of the spheres of the second model are the hexagonal sections (3.15.1) of the lattice cubes (full lines) of the first model, displaced by the length of half an edge of the lattice cube.

4.8. Methods of Modelling Surfaces

Models of surfaces are to be seen in most mathematical libraries and museums. The majority of these are made of plaster of Paris, which is not an easy material for the amateur to handle. If it is desired to attempt the construction of a plaster solid, the best material to use is 'Pioneer' plaster, or a similar slow-setting compound, which gives plenty of time for manipulation and can if necessary, when practically set, be carved with a knife. It may take a day or more to set fully hard.

It is best to build up some kind of ground-work first. A surface designed to rest on a flat base can be built up in contoured layers of wood, plaster-board, or similar material, and the plaster employed only to fill in the gaps. This is the best way to make a plaster relief-map where contours can be traced from flat maps. For a more general surface a ground-work of wire or gauze can often be improvised. For example, in the case of Steiner's Quartic, described in 4.6, a framework of wire circles joined by the axes may well be made the starting-point. Some guide for the moulding of the surface is almost a necessity. Alternatively the surface can be cast in a mould of papier-mâché or layers of plaster-board; it should be smoothed down after a few hours with a knife, and finally, when fully set, with coarse glass-paper.

Modelling-clay is more suitable for the amateur; it can be fired if it is desired to make the model permanent. Plasticine can be used for temporary models. Here again for accurate work a ground-work is desirable.

4.8.1. Functions of two variables. The surface representing $z = f(x,y)$ can be modelled in several ways. The simplest method is to mark out the (x,y)-plane on a cork or wooden base-board and erect knitting-pins, hat-pins, or straws of the appropriate lengths at points corresponding to definite values of x and y. Integral values will usually be sufficient.

A better method is an extension of the idea employed in 4.3.5 to build the quadrics from their circular sections. It consists of constructing cardboard sections which are interlocked in the same manner as the partitions in an egg-box. Consider as an example the surface given by $z = x^2 - y^2 + 10$. The vertical section through XOX' is $z = x^2 + 10$ (corresponding to $y = 0$). This is drawn on card and cut out; the ordinates at $x = 2, 1, 0, -1, -2$ are cut through from the base for just over half their heights. The vertical sections, parallel to this one, corresponding to $y = \pm 1$, $y = \pm 2$ are constructed in the same way: their curves are $z = x^2 + 9$, $z = x^2 + 6$, and time is saved by using a template of the curve $z = x^2$, which can be used for all. The sections perpendicular to these, corresponding to the values $0, \pm 1, \pm 2$ of x, and whose curves are

$$z = -y^2 + 10, \quad z = -y^2 + 11, \quad z = -y^2 + 14,$$

are now constructed, but the ordinates here are cut *from the top* down to just over half-way. If the cardboard is thick, the cuts will have to be widened, but otherwise the sections can be slipped easily into place. Lastly, the four outermost sections, whose curves are $z = x^2+1$, $z = -y^2+19$, are made and fitted into place. These need only two cuts each, as shown,

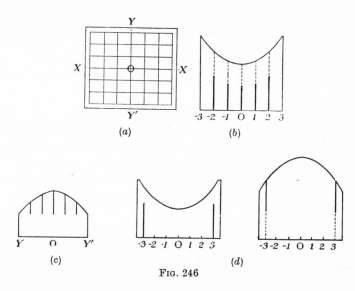

Fig. 246

as they surround the whole. If it is considered desirable the interior can be filled with clay or concrete. A suitable scale for this model is 1 inch for x and y units and $\frac{1}{4}$ inch for the z unit.

Another method is to build up horizontal layers of wood cut to the shape of successive contours. The curves corresponding to the values $z = 1, 2, 3,..., 18, 19$ are

$$x^2-y^2 = -9, \qquad x^2-y^2 = -8, \qquad ...,$$

$$x^2-y^2 = 8, \qquad x^2-y^2 = 9.$$

The curves can be drawn on squared paper glued to three-ply wood and cut out with a fret-saw. Modelling clay or putty can be used to round-off the steps, but it is not necessary.

Alternatively, we can construct the sections of a surface by planes $z =$ constant and cut them out of cardboard for equal intervals of z over the range desired for the model. Draw on these sections lines parallel to an axis, say the x-axis, at equal intervals of y, and cut slots in them from the edge of the section inwards for a fixed distance. Now on another set of cards prepare the sections by the planes $y =$ constant, at the same

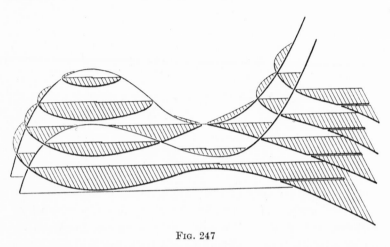

Fig. 247

intervals of y. Draw again the lines parallel to the x-axis and slot them to within the fixed distance of the edge, so that they can be pushed into the slots of the other cards, and so build up the surface by means of a rectangular network of cards as before. See Fig. 247, where a cubic surface of the form

$$z = x^2(x-3) - y^2$$

is shown under construction in this way. This surface can be conveniently made from $z = -2$ to 6. Other surfaces suitable for sectional construction are

$$z = (x^2+y^2-c^2) - 4c^2x^2$$

and $$z = x(x^2-3y^2),$$

from $z = -3$ to $+3$. This last is a surface called the monkey-saddle, because it has a third depression for the tail.

4.8.2. Use of glass plates. The same principle can be carried out in a different way. The sections of the surface by the planes $z =$ constant can be drawn with a chinagraph pencil on glass plates—lantern-slide cover-glasses are excellent for the purpose and can be obtained very cheaply—which are then mounted in parallel planes. For a single model the glass plates

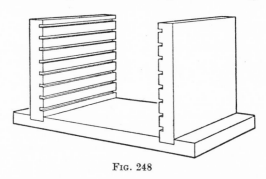

Fig. 248

can be spaced by slats of wood along opposite edges—wooden spills will serve—and clamped together. But if a number of surfaces are to be shown a wooden rack can easily be used, either a photographic plate-drying rack, or a home-made article which can be constructed by cutting parallel horizontal grooves in two vertical side-pieces as in Fig. 248. The eye integrates the sections into a surface quite satisfactorily if the interval is not too great.

4.8.3. Use of a lathe. Obviously any solid of revolution can be turned on a lathe; the construction is facilitated by cutting a template with its edge in the form of the curve whose rotation generates the solid. If the tool can be traversed at an angle to the axis, a cone can be cut mechanically; if, which is rarely possible, the cutter can be moved along a line skew to the axis, the one-sheeted hyperboloid will be produced.

4.9. Puzzles

Many books and articles on mathematical puzzles have appeared in recent years and we do not propose to give a full account of them here. But a small collection of models of the 'puzzle' type will add considerably to the interest of any mathematical display, so that we shall describe a few.

4.9.1. Solid dissections. We begin with a few simple examples.

(a) *A cube dissected into three pyramids.* Make three solids from the net shown in the diagram: they can be fitted together very easily to form a cube. This gives another method of showing the formula for the volume of a pyramid.

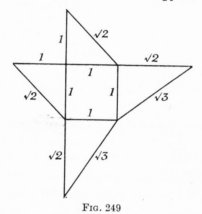

Fig. 249

(b) Slightly harder is the dissection of the tetrahedron into four congruent pieces. The net for one of these is given. Make four of these; they take a little fitting together.

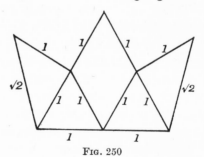

Fig. 250

(c) *The Soma cube.* This is a $3 \times 3 \times 3$ cube dissected into six pieces composed of 4 unit cubes and one piece of 3 unit cubes. They are shown in the diagram. The puzzle is first to put them together to form a cube, and then to make a wide variety of other shapes. A full account has been given by Martin Gardner (*Scientific American*, Sept. 1958).

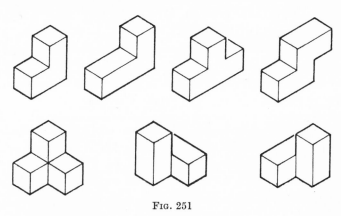

FIG. 251

(d) Steinhaus's dissected cube is also a $3 \times 3 \times 3$ cube, but cut into six pieces, three of 5 unit cubes, and three of 4 unit cubes (Fig. 252). There are just two ways of fitting them together to form a cube; the puzzle is a very difficult one. First use three pieces to make a stepped pyramid like one of the units in (a) above. There are two ways of doing this, with the same three pieces. The completion of the cube is unique.

(e) A very interesting dissection puzzle takes its origin from the arithmetical fact that $3^3 + 4^3 + 5^3 = 6^3$. The problem of dissecting the $6 \times 6 \times 6$ cube to display this was solved some years ago and the solution was published in *Eureka*, the magazine of the Cambridge Archimedeans.† It makes a good puzzle. There are eight pieces; the $3 \times 3 \times 3$ cube is uncut; there is a $2 \times 2 \times 2$ cube, a block $2 \times 1 \times 1$, another $3 \times 2 \times 1$, and four others. One of these is a $4 \times 4 \times 4$ with a $2 \times 1 \times 1$ block cut from its corner; the others are shown in Fig. 253. The assembly of the $4 \times 4 \times 4$ cube is obvious; five pieces make the

† An undergraduate mathematical society.

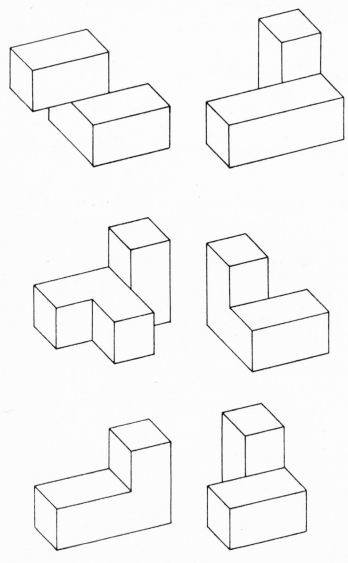

Fɪɢ. 252

$5 \times 5 \times 5$ cube, and the whole set can be assembled to make the $6 \times 6 \times 6$ cube.

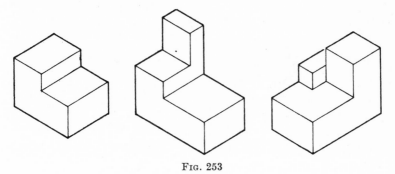

FIG. 253

4.9.2. Flexagons. These are polygons of flat card, hinged together by their edges to form loops. They can be manipulated by folding so as to display hidden faces. The first is rather different from the others. This is simply a chain of four squares joined by opposite edges, and also creased along each diagonal. The puzzle is to turn it inside out, so as to display the inner faces of the squares, which should be coloured differently. There are supposed to be a number of ways of doing this, but we have only discovered one.

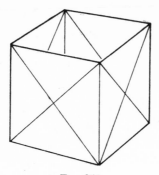

FIG. 254

The hexaflexagon family. A full account of these has been given by R. F. Wheeler (*Math. Gazette*, **42** (1958), 1). We have only space here to describe the most interesting original pair, and the reader must be referred to Mr. Wheeler's article or to articles

in *The Scientific American* (May 1958)† for an account of their
numerous and fascinating progeny. These two are both constructed from straight strips of paper—gum-strip used double,
with the gummed surfaces stuck together, serves very well.
The first (F_1, Fig. 255) needs ten equilateral triangles, the
second (F_4) nineteen. In each case one triangle is used for stick-

FIG. 255

ing the ends of the chain together. The triangles should now
be coloured so as to display the flexagon's interesting properties.
We adopt Mr. Wheeler's ingenious system of colouring, and
his notation. *Italic* letters give the colours on the underside.
F_1 needs three primary colours, red, blue, and yellow. The symbol Δ indicates the blank faces which are due to be stuck
together. When the strip has been creased on all lines and
coloured, we fold it in such a way as to conceal one of the
colours, by twisting it always in the same sense of rotation, and
finally join the ends. The result is a flat hexagon showing two
colours, one on each side. It can be 'pinched' and opened out
flat again to show a new colour; any two of the three colours
can be displayed.

F_4 gets interesting. The notation is as before, but now we
need three other colours; Mr. Wheeler suggests the secondary
colours: green, orange, and violet. The strip is first folded so
as to hide all the secondary colours, which reduces it to the
first case F_1; this is then folded as before and stuck. It will now
be found that the secondary colours can only be displayed by
pinching and flexing in a position where the two corresponding

† Reprinted in Martin Gardner's book; see Bibliography.

primary colours are visible; such a position can be flexed in two different ways, one of which leads to the secondary colour and the other goes round the primary cycle shown by F_1. The interested flexer can probably unravel further complications for himself; if not, he should read Wheeler's article.

The tetraflexagon family. It has recently been pointed out by P. B. Chapman (*Math. Gazette*, **45** (Oct. 1961), no. 353) that the same process can be carried out with squares instead of hexagons. We shall describe only one member of the family. Take a square of paper measuring four units on a side and mark it out in unit squares. Cut out and remove the central 2×2 square. Beginning at a corner, colour the remaining twelve squares in order round the 'frame' according to the following scheme: $O(V)$, $O(B)$, $R(G)$, $Y(G)$, $Y(B)$, $R(V)$, $O(V)$, $O(B)$, $R(G)$, $Y(G)$, $Y(B)$, $R(V)$. (Letters in brackets denote colours on the back.) Now fold three consecutive edges of the square inwards in turn, all the same way. A rectangle 3×2 results. The final corner has now to be folded the opposite way with a twist, so as to bring all four squares of one colour on one side, and all four squares of the other colour on the other. It can then be flexed up or down about either axis of symmetry to reveal the other colours. There will always be three thicknesses at each corner. The reader is invited to experiment on the same lines as with the hexaflexagons.

Historical note. Flexagons were first discovered and named by A. H. Stone, a graduate of Cambridge University, while working at Princeton in 1939. With J. W. Tukey and others he worked out the full theory, but owing to the intervention of war it was never published. Since then the mathematical grapevine has carried flexagons around the world, and many independent investigations have been made, but the credit for their origination must go to Stone and his team. Stone also shared in another contribution to less serious mathematics, being a member of the team who first discovered a dissection of a square into a set of unequal squares with integral sides. See, for example, Steinhaus, *Mathematical Snapshots*, p. 7.

V

MECHANICAL MODELS

5.1. MODELS IN MECHANICS

IT is not intended in this book to give any account of the apparatus available for teaching mechanics, which can be found described in manufacturers' catalogues and in textbooks. Because of its associations with the science department, this branch of mathematics has for long given an honoured place to practical work. A caveat may, however, not be out of place here: in the authors' experience, the simpler the apparatus used the better. The best aid to mechanical understanding is intelligent observation of everyday happenings. The window-frame, the bicycle, the hanging picture, the railway train, and the sailing-ship give more insight into the principles of mechanics, and certainly more appreciation of the complexity of real phenomena, and the great simplification brought about by abstraction, than any number of pulleys, strings, and trolleys designed to show special laws. Models of pulley-systems are useful, but more impressive is the real thing—a builder's hoist, the tackles on a main-sheet, or the Weston pulley in the goods-yard.

The models described in the following pages are worth making for a different reason; either because they are paradoxical, and provoke thought and discussion, or because they are of geometrical interest and worth studying at close quarters.

5.1.1. The cone that runs uphill. This is a well-known paradox, the principle of which is simple and the performance surprising. A roller is made by uniting two congruent circular cones by their bases. It is placed on two inclined tracks meeting at an acute angle. This angle is sufficiently great for the axle of the cone actually to descend while it appears to roll up the incline (see Fig. 256). If α is the semivertical angle of each cone, β the inclination of the tracks to the horizontal, and γ the angle between them (in a horizontal plane), the condition for this is $\sin \gamma > \sin \beta \cot \alpha$. A suitable value of γ is easily found by trial.

To make a model, the cone can be turned from solid wood, or made hollow out of cardboard sectors which are glued to the central circular disk. Alternatively two plastic funnels can be cemented together by their rims, or two small conical flasks can be cemented together by their bases. Flat plywood slats will

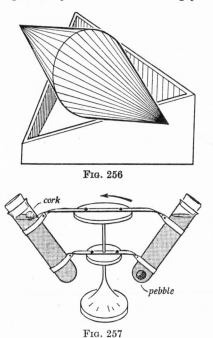

FIG. 256

FIG. 257

serve for the inclines, standing on their edges, and joined at the head and foot with plywood cross-pieces.

5.1.2. The centrifuge. This is an instrument widely used today to increase the rate of sedimentation of suspensions; in the form of the cream-separator it is tolerably familiar. A model which demonstrates clearly the effects of acceleration on a system can be made which is both simple and convincing. Fig. 257 shows such a model, made from wooden toy-wheels, metal strip, and a bill-file. The two test tubes are filled with water; one contains a cork and the other a small lead bob or a round pebble. When the model is rotated, the pebble rises, as might be expected, but the cork sinks, which at first is hard to understand.

5.1.3. A friction paradox. Two rollers are mounted on perpendicular axles in different planes. An endless thread passes round them and connects them, both directly and with a cross-over, as shown in the diagram (Fig. 258). The instrument is somewhat capricious, but the following phenomena can be demonstrated with it.

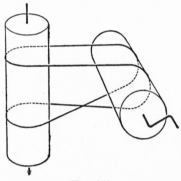

FIG. 258

(*a*) One roller is rotated continuously in one direction. The other starts in one direction, but if temporarily stopped with the finger continues in the opposite direction.

(*b*) One roller is rotated to and fro through a small angle. The other roller rotates continuously in the same direction.

The apparatus shows that dynamical friction is less than statical, but a full explanation is complicated, if indeed it is possible, and certainly involves consideration of the elasticity of the connecting belt.

5.1.4. Non-circular rollers. There is only one curve of constant *radius*, the circle. An efficient wheel, mounted on a fixed axle, must therefore be circular. But it is not generally realized that the circle is not the only curve with constant *width*. In fact there are infinitely many such curves, and a wide variety of forms is possible for an efficient *roller*.

A simple example can be constructed by taking an equilateral triangle and describing on each side an arc whose centre is at the opposite vertex (Fig. 259). It is easily seen that the width (defined as the distance between parallel tangents) is constant and equal to the radius of the arcs. This curve has *points de rebroussement* where the gradient is discontinuous, but this is easily avoided as shown in the second diagram: all the arcs are centred at the vertices of the triangle.

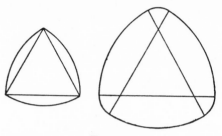

FIG. 259

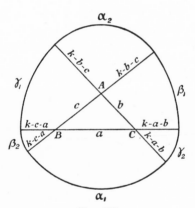

FIG. 260

More generally, a curve of this type can be constructed from any triangle ABC as follows (see Fig. 260).

Draw an arc α_1 with centre A and radius $k-a$

and   ,, α_2 ,, A ,, $k-b-c$.

Then draw   ,, β_1 ,, B ,, $k-b$,

             ,, β_2 ,, B ,, $k-c-a$,

             ,, γ_1 ,, C ,, $k-c$,

             ,, γ_2 ,, C ,, $k-a-b$,

where k is arbitrary, but greater than the sum of any two sides of the triangle.

It is evident, from the fact that

radius of α_1+radius of α_2 = radius of β_1+radius of β_2
= radius of γ_1+radius of γ_2

that these arcs form a closed curve with constant width $2(k-s) = d$, say. Further, the total length of this curve is

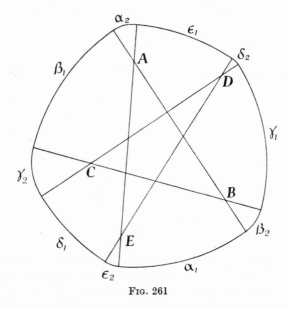

Fig. 261

the same as that of a circle of diameter d. For the length of α_1 and α_2 together is Ad, and so on; thus the total length is

$$(A+B+C)d = \pi d.$$

This last property is true for all curves of constant width.

Instead of the triangle ABC we may take any odd number of vertices forming a convex polygon; Fig. 261 shows the construction for five vertices $ABCDE$, joined by a pentagon.

It is interesting to make a model of some of these rollers. Cut the curves out of plywood in congruent pairs and mount them on axles to which they are rigidly bolted. A flat board resting on the rollers can then be rolled along quite level in its own plane, but the rollers themselves move in a curiously irregular manner.

There is a three-dimensional analogue in the form of a 'tetrahedron' bounded by triangular spherical caps and toroidal strips, but it is difficult to make.

5.1.5. Parabola and catenary. These curves are of frequent occurrence in everyday life, and a model can easily be set up to show the difference between them. The parabola appears in the path of a cricket ball, the shape of the suspension-bridge cable, and the parabolic reflector; the catenary is seen in the

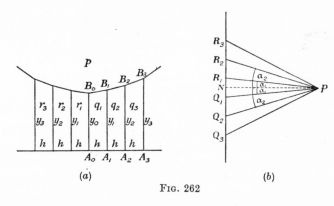

FIG. 262

hanging chain, telegraph wire or electric transmission line, and in the curve of a sail, or a cylindrical soap-film stretched between two plane circular ends.

In the case of the catenary, the load is distributed uniformly along the length of the chain. For the suspension bridge, however, the ideal arrangement is to have the uniform horizontal load supported evenly by the vertical ties. It is easy to show that in this case the points of attachment of these ties to the hanging chain lie on a parabola.

Suppose there is a central tie $A_0 B_0$ (Fig. 262 (a)), and let $A_1 B_1$, $A_2 B_2$, etc., be vertical ties at equal horizontal distances h. Draw the reciprocal diagram, Fig. 262 (b). The vertical steps $R_3 R_2$, $R_2 R_1$, $R_1 Q_1$, $Q_1 Q_2$,... are all equal, being equal to the vertical loads in the ties. Thus the slopes of PQ_1, PQ_2, etc., which are the slopes of $B_0 B_1$, $B_1 B_2$, etc., are in arithmetic progression:

$$\tan N\widehat{P}Q_r = k(r-\tfrac{1}{2}).$$

Therefore we have

$$y_r - y_{r-1} = kh(r - \tfrac{1}{2}),$$

$$\cdots \cdots \cdots$$

$$y_1 - y_0 = \tfrac{1}{2}kh.$$

Therefore, by addition, $y_r - y_0 = \dfrac{kh}{2} \sum_{1}^{r} (2r - 1) = \dfrac{kh}{2} r^2.$

Thus the points B_r lie on the parabola $y = kx^2/2h$, with vertex at B_0.

The heavy snake-like chains used for key-chains and watch-chains make excellent catenaries; a heavy cord can be used, but is apt not to be uniformly flexible, and a chain of small links is better. A suspension bridge can be made for comparison by hanging a heavy horizontal rod by fine threads from a similar cord or chain. This needs accurate work in measuring and fastening the threads, but is very effective if well done. Mark off a series of equal intervals on the rod, beginning at the centre and working outwards in each direction. Attach a thread to the rod at each mark. If l is the length of the centre thread, the others should be, proceeding in order from the centre, $l + k \cdot 1^2, l + k \cdot 2^2, l + k \cdot 3^2$, etc., where k is any convenient length. (For a 3-foot span, with threads every $1\frac{1}{2}$ inches, $k = \frac{1}{10}$ inch gives a reasonable sag of 14·4 inches.) At exactly these distances along the threads, tie a short cross-bar (a short pin will serve). Hang up the rod by the end threads and adjust a fine chain so that it will hang freely in a catenary in such a way that the two end threads and the centre thread could just be hung from it without disturbing it. Next, shorten the chain so that the centre rises about 0·6 inch with the above measurements (in general, $4h^3/15a^2$, where h = the sag and a = the span); pull down the centre link and hang the centre thread from it. Now raise the other threads in turn, keeping them vertical, and slip the pins through the appropriate links in the chain so that they hang from them. The chain should by this means be pulled out into the parabolic form. Minor adjustments can be made to trim the final curve. An easier method is to hang equal weights at equal horizontal distances along a hanging chain.

If a parabola is cut out of a card and rolled along a line, the path of its focus is a catenary. This cannot be seen behind the parabola, so it is best to cut the parabola from celluloid or 'Perspex' and mark the focus by a spot or a small hole.

The paraboloid of revolution, obtained by revolving the parabola about its axis, is the surface taken up by a fluid rotating under gravity. If a torch-bulb is hung at the focus, the property of the parabolic reflector can be shown and the emergent parallel beam of light can be seen in a darkened room. The best results are obtained with mercury, but caution and a slow start are recommended, so that one can be sure that everything is accurately centred before the situation gets out of control. A gramophone turn-table can be used to rotate the beaker or other vessel containing the fluid,† but it must be rigidly and centrally fixed to it.

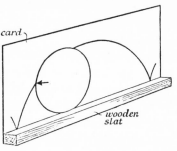

Fig. 263

The catenoid, i.e. the surface formed by rotating a catenary about its directrix, is a *minimal* surface, having minimum area within a given boundary. This is the form taken up by a soap-film spanning two coaxial circular disks. Other minimal-surface problems can be demonstrated with soap-films; a full account is given in *What is Mathematics?* by Courant and Robbins, chap. vii, § 11.

5.1.6. Cycloid. The cycloid is the path traced out by a point on the circumference of a circle which rolls on a straight line. It can be demonstrated very easily from the definition. Take a wooden slat about a foot long and ¼-inch square and glue a card to the back by its lower edge. A circular disk can now be rolled down the slat and the cycloid traced on the card (Fig. 263).

The cycloid has two famous mechanical properties. Christian Huygens discovered that it is a true *tautochrone*; that is to say

† A tin of golden syrup will serve.

that a particle moving under gravity on a cycloid, with its arch downwards and cusps upwards, will execute exact simple harmonic motion, and therefore describe paths of different amplitude in equal times. Jacques Bernoulli proved that in this same position it is also a *brachistochrone*; i.e. it is the path along which a particle can travel from one point (the cusp) to a lower point under gravity in the shortest possible time.

These properties can both be demonstrated by constructing a cycloidal track on which a ball can roll. This is most easily

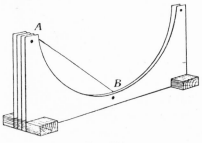

Fig. 264

set up by cutting two plywood sheets and spacing them with washers (see Fig. 264). A straight incline can be made for comparison; the time taken for a ball to travel from *A* to *B* along the cycloid will be less than along the straight line *AB*.

5.2. Models in Statistics

The chief adjuncts to a study of statistics are packs of cards, sets of dice, coins, to say nothing of roulette wheels, football pools, racing odds, totalizators, and other apparatus providing the gambler with his thrills and the bookmaker with his money. Many statistical experiments require the tossing of large numbers of coins, and for this purpose mechanical assistance is useful.

5.2.1. A simple coin-tossing machine. This consists of a box to contain the coins, roomy enough for the number required to lie on the bottom without overlapping, and deep enough for them not to jump out when tossed. The top is open for observations; if a hinged lid is provided, the box can be shallower. The bottom of the box is perforated with a large number of holes. A movable board beneath carries pins on its upper surface which project through the holes when the board is raised and strike the coins on the under side. This board is pivoted amidships, so that a blow on the other end raises it and tosses the coins (see Fig. 265).

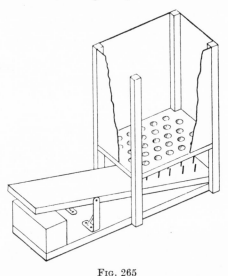

Fig. 265

5.2.2. The Galton Quincunx. Suppose a steel ball rolls down a line of greatest slope of an inclined board, and strikes a pin in its path. It is not difficult to imagine conditions in which it has an equal chance of rebounding to the left or right of the pin. If two pins are now placed on a horizontal line lower down the board and the angle of slope is correctly adjusted, the ball will hit one or other of them after it rebounds from the first pin. Again it may happen that for small variations of its path it has equal chances of falling to left or right of these pins.

The probabilities therefore of falling to the left of both, between them, or to the right of both, should be in the proportion 1:2:1. The process can be continued and it is plain that the probabilities of a ball passing between the different pins of a row are proportional to the numbers in Pascal's Triangle:

$$
\begin{array}{ccccccccc}
 & & & & 1 & & & & \\
 & & & 1 & & 1 & & & \\
 & & 1 & & 2 & & 1 & & \\
 & 1 & & 3 & & 3 & & 1 & \\
1 & & 4 & & 6 & & 4 & & 1
\end{array}
$$

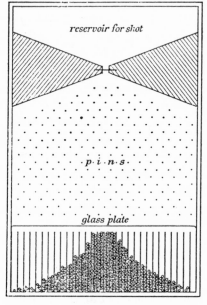

Fig. 266

The distribution of probabilities along the nth row is thus proportional to the coefficients in $(1+t)^n$. Such a distribution is called a binomial distribution.

A board of this kind is called a Galton Quincunx, after the name of its inventor;† *quincunx* is the Latin name for the 5 (: · :) on a die, or any similar pattern: for example, trees in an orchard. An example is shown in Fig. 266. Steel balls or lead shot may be used, and the partitions at the base are of such a height that two balls cannot rest on one another. A glass plate lies on top to prevent this. The board is first tilted so that the

† Francis Galton, *Natural Inheritance*, 1889.

balls run into the reservoir shown at the top of the diagram, the gate being removed. The gate is then replaced and the board tilted like a bagatelle board. When the gate is removed the balls roll down and are deflected by the pins into the compartments at the bottom. If the angle is suitably adjusted, the numbers in the compartments can be made to approximate closely to the binomial distribution. For large numbers of both shot and rows of pins this distribution approximates to the standard error curve $y = ke^{-x^2/2s^2}$, where k and s are constants. The curve formed by the columns of shot in the compartments should therefore give a rough idea of its shape.

5.2.3. Statistical evaluation of π.

If a stick of length l is thrown at random onto a surface ruled with parallel lines whose distance apart is a $(> l)$, then the probability of its crossing a line is $2l/\pi a$. For if its centre falls at a distance x from a line, and it makes an angle θ with the direction of the lines, it will cross a line if $x < \frac{1}{2}l\sin\theta$.

Therefore for this value of θ, assuming all values of x from 0 to $\frac{1}{2}a$ equally likely, the probability that it crosses a line is $l\sin\theta/a$. Hence the total probability, averaging over all θ, is

$$\int_0^\pi \frac{l\sin\theta}{a}\, d\theta \bigg/ \int_0^\pi d\theta = \frac{l}{\pi a}\int_0^\pi \sin\theta\, d\theta = \frac{2l}{\pi a}.$$

[We assume $l < a$, otherwise for certain values of θ the result is a certainty and the average will be different.] In practice it is best to choose l about $\frac{3}{4}a$ so that the probability is about $\frac{1}{2}$. To carry out the experiment, matches can be thrown onto paper ruled with equidistant lines, or pencils onto a boarded floor, if the lengths are suitable. Results within about 5 per cent. can be expected from a few hundred trials.

5.3. Plane Linkages

There is something very attractive about the motion of a linkage of rods. Who, for example, is not fascinated by the sight of the connecting-rods of a locomotive, especially one adorned with an external Walschaerts or Stephenson valve-gear? Not only is the study of link-motion a useful and important part of kinematics, it also introduces several interesting loci and envelopes and brings in geometrical constructions and analytical geometry.

Linkages can be constructed in several ways. The simplest is to cut strips from cardboard (about 10-sheet), and join them with paper-fasteners, or drawing-pins with points uppermost. A more permanent model can be made from steel strapping— the sort that is put round crates and is usually thrown away. This can be drilled and joined with metal eyelets, stationers' or shoemakers'. For exhibition purposes the links can be made from metal strip, joined with bolts and stop-nuts, lacquered, and mounted permanently on a board. If two or more links are to be equal in length, drill them simultaneously.

5.3.1. Approximate straight-line motions. Foremost in historic interest is the problem of producing straight-line motion by linkwork. Before the days of straight guides it was difficult to maintain true linear motion, e.g. in the pistons of beam engines. The earliest attempts produced a motion which was only approximately linear, but they were in their day a great step forward. James Watt is said to have been more proud of his link-motion, which he discovered in 1784, than of his steam-engine.

The approximate straight-line motions have this in common, that they are all three-bar linkages. Two equal bars hinged to fixed points are hinged to the ends of a third bar. A point P carried by this bar generates the approximate straight line. In fact it generates a sextic curve, which may be very nearly straight in the neighbourhood of an inflexion. It is necessary to have at least five bars for exact straight-line motion (Hart and Kempe, 1877).

5.3.1 (*a*). The first motion is *James Watt*'s (1784), shown in Fig. 267. Bars AC and DB are equal, and P is the mid-point of CD. The path of P approximates more closely to a straight line as the bars AC and BD are lengthened. If

$$AB = CD$$
$$= \sqrt{2}\,AC = \sqrt{2}\,BD,$$

P describes Bernoulli's lemniscate.

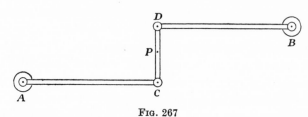

FIG. 267

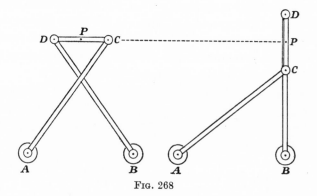

FIG. 268

5.3.1 (*b*). *Tchebycheff*'s motion (1850) is shown in Fig. 268. Here $AC = DB = 5a$, $AB = 4a$, $CD = 2a$, and P is the mid-point of CD. The height of P above AB is $4a$ both when CD is horizontal and also in the two positions when CD is vertical.

5.3.1 (*c*). *Roberts*'s motion (1860) is a still closer approximation (Fig. 269). Here $AC = BD = CP = PD$, and $CD = \frac{1}{2}AB$. P is carried by the plate. P lies on AB again in the central and the two extreme positions. AC/CD must exceed $\frac{1}{4}(\sqrt{33}-1)$.

5.3.2. Exact straight-line motion. The first successful solution of the problem of exact linear motion was put forward

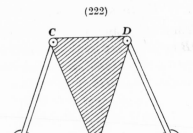

Fig. 269

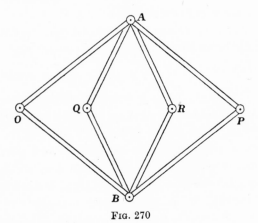

Fig. 270

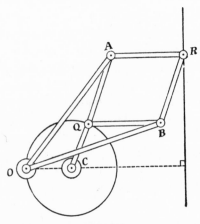

Fig. 271

by Peaucellier, an officer in the French Army, in 1864.† The linkwork he used was afterwards employed to control the pumps in the ventilation system for the Houses of Parliament.

Kempe, a London barrister, who also succeeded in solving the problem, published a book in 1877 with the alluring title *How to draw a Straight Line*, in which the following linkages are described.

5.3.2 (*a*). *Peaucellier's* linkage, which is much the most efficient in practice, is essentially an inversor, and can be used for many other purposes. It has two forms (see Fig. 270). $OAPB$, $QARB$ are two rhombi of hinged rods with a common diagonal AB. $OQRP$ are therefore collinear. It can be proved without difficulty by Pythagoras's Theorem that

$$OQ.PQ = OQ.OR = OA^2 - AQ^2 = \text{constant}.$$

Hence if O is fixed, Q and R describe inverse curves, and if Q is fixed O and P describe inverse curves (with an imaginary radius of inversion).

Now the inverse of a circle with respect to a point on its circumference is a straight line. Therefore if we add another link of any length r connecting Q with a point C fixed in the plane, and fix O so that $OC = r$, Q will describe part of a circle through O, and R will describe a straight line (Fig. 271). Alternatively we could fix Q and make O describe a circle through Q; P would then trace out a line.

5.3.2 (*b*). Another linkage of great importance is the 'crossed parallelogram' $ABCD$ (Fig. 272) in which $AB = CD$, $AD = BC$. This has many uses, including that of an inversor, in which form it was used by *Hart* in 1874 to solve the problem of line motion. If O, P, Q are three fixed points on the rods AB, AD, BC such that OPQ lie on a line parallel to AC, then this will be true in every position of the linkage and $OP.OQ = BQ.QC - OA.OB$ which is constant. Therefore once again, if O is fixed, we have a means of producing inverse curves, but this time with only four bars instead of six. One extra bar suffices to make P move on

† Mr. Michael Goldberg has pointed out that strictly priority could be claimed by Sarrus, whose three-dimensional solution (5.4.4) dates from 1853.

a circle through O, so that Q describes a straight line. This is the smallest number of bars for a linkage giving line-motion.

We shall now describe another five-bar linkage which solves the problem; this is also due to *Hart*.

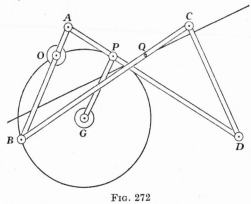

Fɪɢ. 272

5.3.2 (*c*). The bars AB, CD (Fig. 273) are equal, as also are BP, DP. Points E, F are taken on AB, CD so that $BE = DF$ and
$$BE . BA = BP^2.$$

These points E, F are joined by a rod of length equal to BP or DP, and A, C are fixed in the plane so that $AC = AB = CD$. Then P traces out the perpendicular bisector of AC. The proof of this is an interesting exercise in similar triangles.

5.3.2 (*d*). Two other line-motion linkages based on the Peaucellier and Hart inversors, but involving quite a different principle, are due to *Kempe* (1875). In the first (Fig. 274), A and C are fixed to the plane and $AOBC$ is a rhombus. The rods RA, RB, RQ are equal and P is chosen to make the kites $OARB$, $RQPB$ similar; i.e. $PQ = PB$ and $BP.BO = BR^2$. Then it can be proved without difficulty that $Q\widehat{A}C$ is a right angle, so that Q describes a straight line perpendicular to AC.

The second linkage (Fig. 275) uses two similar crossed parallelograms in the same way as the first uses two similar kites. These are $ABCD$, $ADEF$ in the figure, where $AB = CD = AQ$, $AD = BC = EF$, $AF = DE = DA^2/DC$. Then $Q\widehat{A}D = B\widehat{A}D$

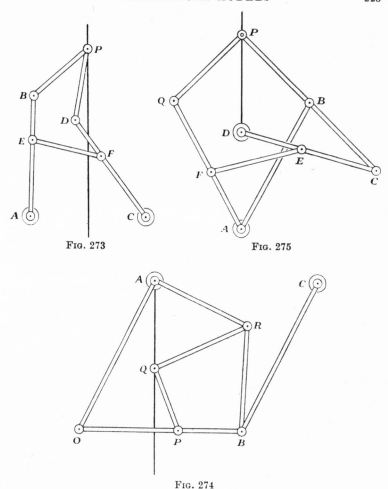

FIG. 273   FIG. 275

FIG. 274

in all positions. If therefore we fix A and D and attach P by equal rods to B and Q, P must move along the line AD produced. These straight-line linkages are illustrated in Plate 4b.

5.3.3 Linkages for drawing curves.

It was proved by Kempe in 1875 that any algebraic curve can be described by a linkage. Even for so simple a curve as a conic the linkage is quite complicated, with nine bars: the motion of a suitable point on a crossed parallelogram is inverted with a Peaucellier cell.

There are, however, certain quartic curves for which the link-work is remarkably simple.

5.3.3 (a). *Bernoulli's lemniscate.* The linkwork invented by James Watt will draw the lemniscate when it forms a crossed parallelogram with the long bar $\sqrt{2}$ times as long as the shorter bars (see 5.3.1 (a) above and Fig. 276). Alternatively, the lemni-

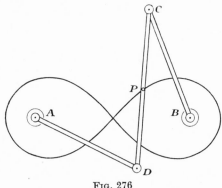

Fig. 276

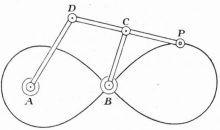

Fig. 277

scate can be described by the point P (Fig. 277) on a kite $ABCD$ in which $AB = \sqrt{2}\,BC$.

5.3.3 (b). *Cassinian oval.* If in this last figure a Peaucellier cell is added as shown in Fig. 278, the points Q, Q' will describe a Cassinian oval with foci at A and at the image of A in B.

5.3.3 (c). *Limaçon.* In Fig. 275, add a bar AD, and fix E, F instead of A, D. Then the locus of B is a limaçon. If, in addition, $EC = 2BC$, then the locus is a cardioid (shown in Fig. 279).

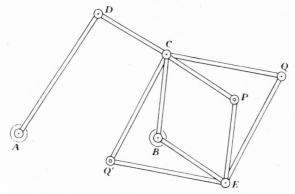

Fig. 278

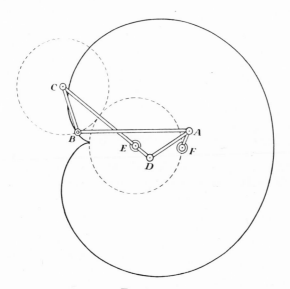

Fig. 279

The limaçons can however be drawn more simply if a sliding rod is used, as shown in Fig. 280. The rod BAP slides through a guide pivoted at B, while A moves on a circle with centre O. If the complete curve is required, an arrangement similar to that shown in Fig. 17 must be adopted at B. Since the limaçon is the inverse of a conic with respect to a focus, this gives an alternative method of generating a conic by a linkage, by fixing a Peaucellier cell across B and P.

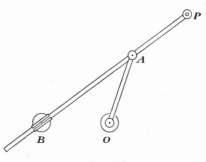

Fɪɢ. 280

5.3.4. Trisection of the angle.

If, in the linkage of Fig. 280, we take $OA = AP = a$, then if PO is produced to C, $\widehat{BOC} = 3\widehat{BPO}$. Thus if O, B are connected by a rod of length a and removed from the plane, we have an instrument with which to solve the trisection problem. This is *Pascal's Trisector*. It is better for this purpose to make the end B of the rod OB run in a slot in the rod PAB. The diagram (Fig. 281) shows the instrument in use for trisecting a given angle BOC.

There are many other instruments for trisection. The simplest (apart from the marked straight-edge) is probably the T-*square*. This consists of two rods joined rigidly together at right angles; the shorter (MLN, Fig. 282) is bisected at the joint. This requires a preliminary construction. If BOC is the angle to be trisected, draw a line XY parallel to OB at a distance equal to LN or LM. This can itself be done with the aid of the square, by laying KL along OB, marking two positions of M, and joining them.

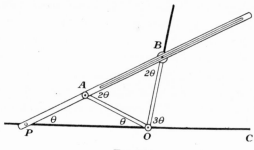

Fig. 281

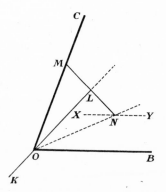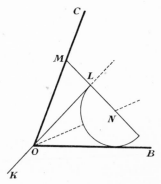

Fig. 282

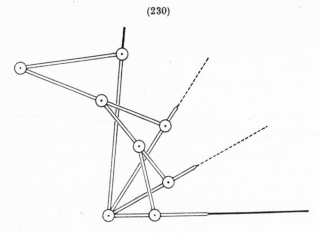

FIG. 283

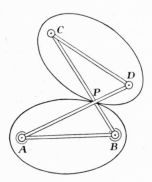
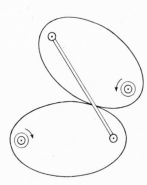

FIG. 284

Then place the square so that KL passes through O, M lies on OC, and N on XY. ON and OL are then the angle-trisectors.

The *Tomahawk*, which is the T-square with the semicircle with centre N and radius NL rigidly attached to it, can be used directly without previously drawing the line XY (Fig. 282, r.).

The principle of similar crossed parallelograms employed in Kempe's linkage (Fig. 275) can be extended to make an angle-trisector. For this we need three similar crossed parallelograms, the long arm of each being a short arm of its successor. The resulting apparatus is shown in Fig. 283. This principle can obviously be extended to the construction of an apparatus for the division of an angle into any given number of parts.

5.3.5. The crossed parallelogram. The motion of a crossed parallelogram provides in itself an introduction to a variety of geometrical topics. Suppose first of all we fix one of the short bars AB (Fig. 284). Since the points C, D are now rotating about B and A respectively, the *instantaneous centre* for the motion of the rod CD is the point P, the intersection of BC and AD. Evidently $AP+PB = CP+PD = AD$ or BC. Thus the locus of P, considered as a point of space, is the ellipse with A, B as foci and major axis equal to AD; whereas its locus, considered as a point attached to the rod CD, is the equal ellipse with C, D as foci. Furthermore, since the tangent to an ellipse at any point is equally inclined to the focal distances, these two ellipses touch at P in every position of the rods. The motion of CD is therefore generated by the rolling of the second ellipse on the first, which remains fixed. These are the *body-centrode* and the *space-centrode* respectively for the motion of CD.

Again, if the angular velocity of AD is ω, the angular velocity of CD is $\omega \dfrac{AD}{PD}$ in the same sense, and the rate of change of the angle CDA is $\omega \dfrac{AP}{PD}$. Now let us replace the rods AB, CD by solid elliptical disks. Retain the link BC, and mount A and D on axles, so obtaining a pair of *elliptical gears*, which are held constantly in mesh by the link BC. The velocity ratio of the pair is

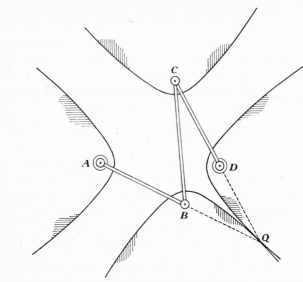

Fɪɢ. 285

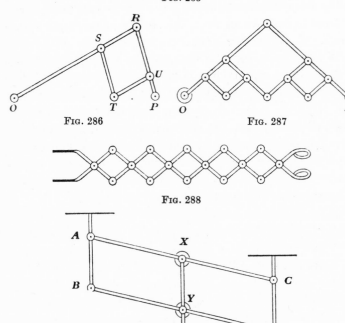

Fɪɢ. 286

Fɪɢ. 287

Fɪɢ. 288

Fɪɢ. 289

AP/PD, which varies from $\dfrac{e}{1-e}$ to $\dfrac{1-e}{e}$ and back again in the course of a revolution, e being the eccentricity of either ellipse. The gear thus provides a 'quick-return' mechanism which finds application in a number of machines.

To make a model, the ellipses can be cut from wooden blocks and should have their rims covered with cloth or felt or strips of corrugated cardboard or metal to prevent slipping. The link BC is essential to ensure contact.

It is instructive to consider the motion of this link itself. Its instantaneous centre is the meet Q of AB and CD produced. Since $QA \sim QD = QC \sim QB = AB$, the locus of Q, regarded as a point of space, is a hyperbola with foci A and D, and regarded as a point of the rod BC, a hyperbola with foci B and C. These hyperbolas are the centrodes for the motion of BC, which is generated by the rolling of the second hyperbola, carrying the rod with it, on the first (Fig. 285).

5.3.6. Miscellaneous linkages. We include here a few additional linkages of interest. The first four are based on the properties of the parallelogram.

5.3.6 (a). *The pantograph.* This familiar mechanism is shown in Fig. 286. The three points O, T, P are collinear. $RSTU$ is a parallelogram, and $PT/TO = PU/UR = $ constant. If any one of the three points O, T, P is kept fixed, the other two describe similar curves. The instrument is used for enlarging or reducing diagrams, and is obtainable from good stationers.

5.3.6 (b). *Dividing machine.* This is an extension of the pantograph (Fig. 287), and is used for dividing a segment OP into equal parts. Extended indefinitely, it becomes

5.3.6 (c). *The 'lazy tongs'* (Fig. 288).

5.3.6 (d). *Roberval's balance* (Fig. 289). This is the familiar letter-weighing machine, or grocer's scales. X, Y are fixed pivots;
$$AB = CD = XY, \qquad AX = XC = BY = YD.$$
The rods AB, CD remain vertical and equidistant from XY; their vertical velocities are always equal and opposite. Consequently, by the principle of zero activity, equal loads will balance, no matter where they are placed on the scale-pans.

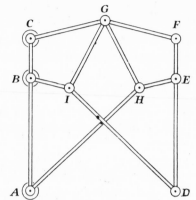

Fig. 290

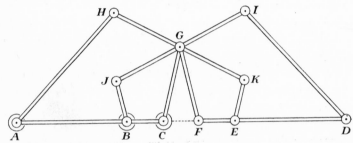

Fig. 291

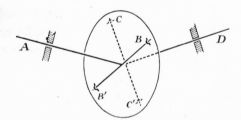

Fig. 292

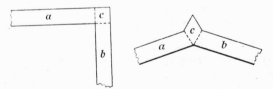

Fig. 293

5.3.6 (*e*). The next two linkages (Figs. 290 and 291) are combinations of double kites to produce parallel motion and sliding motion, and are due to Kempe.

In each case the points A, B, C are fixed, and the larger kites are congruent and similar to the smaller ones, which are also congruent.

In the first figure

$$AC = AH = DF = DI;$$
$$GC = GI = GH = GF;$$
$$BC = BI = HE = EF;$$

and $$CB.CA = CG^2.$$

The rod DEF remains parallel to ABC, and FC is always perpendicular to ABC.

In the second figure

$$AC = AH = DF = DI;$$
$$GC = GJ = GH = GI = GK = GF;$$
$$BC = BJ = EF = EK;$$

and $$CB.CA = CG^2.$$

HGK and IGJ are rigid rods hinged at their mid-points. The rod DEF always moves in the continuation of the line ABC.

5.4. Linkages in Three Dimensions

5.4.1. Hooke's universal joint. This is a very familiar linkage for connecting two rotating shafts which are not quite in the same line.

A model can be easily made of wire and a circular disk in the form shown in Fig. 292. The shafts A and D carry rods BB', CC', rigidly attached to them at right angles. These rods move in hinges attached to the central disk, lying along perpendicular diameters, one on each side.

The motion can also be illustrated even more simply as follows: take an L-shaped piece of cardboard (Fig. 293) and crease it in opposite directions as shown at the corner. The inner edges of portions a and b then represent the two shafts.

5.4.2. 'Inversion' of Hooke's joint. This connects continuous rotary motion with oscillatory rotary motion. The diagram (Fig. 294) explains the joint. A bears an arc of angle α and radius r fixed at right angles to it; D bears a rigid rod OC of length r also fixed to it at right angles; their ends are hinged as shown to a quadrant of a circle of the same radius r; all the hinge-lines pass through O, so that the mechanism is a particular case of what is called a spheric chain. The angle ϕ oscillates

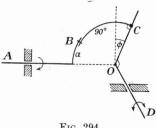

FIG. 294

between $+\alpha$ and $-\alpha$ as A rotates continuously. A wire model is easily made.

5.4.3. Spheric chains. The above joints are described by R. H. Macmillan (*Math. Gazette*, **26** (1942), 5), where the general spheric chain is discussed in detail. A model of it can be made by constructing a polyhedral angle out of thin card; as the angle is deformed by the plane faces hinging about the flexible edges, the outer edges of the angle describe the motion of the general spheric chain. This is one of the cases known in which a closed chain of less than seven links can move. The general chain of six links or less in space is rigid. We proceed to discuss a few of the exceptions.

5.4.4. Sarrus's motion. This is a chain of six bars in which groups of three hinges are parallel or concurrent. The diagrams (Figs. 295 (a), (b), (c)) show examples made from flat card. In Fig. 295 (a) the hinges ac, cd, db are parallel, and so are hinges bf, fe, ea, in a perpendicular direction. In the motion, a and b remain parallel, and XY is always perpendicular to them.

In Fig. 295 (b) the hinges ac, cd, db meet at P and bf, fe, ea at Q. a and b now rotate about PQ. In Fig. 295 (c) the hinges ac, cd, db are parallel, and the other three meet at Q. a moves relative to

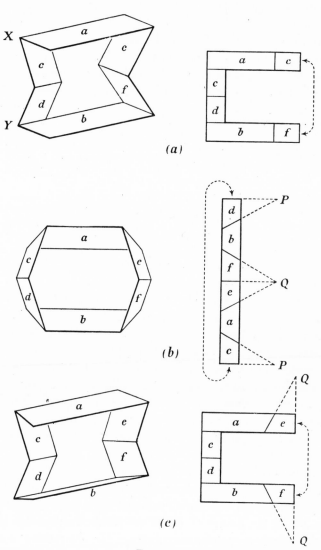

FIG. 295

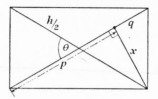

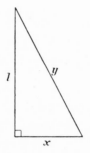

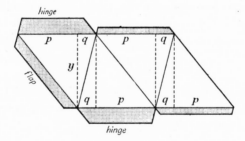

FIG. 296

b by rotating about a line through *Q* parallel to the hinges
ac, cd, db. R. A. Fairthorne (*Math. Gazette,* **28** (1944), 161), to
whom the description of the model of Hooke's joint is due, has
pointed out that these linkages 'seem to be unknown to engineers,
but have been used for centuries by bellows makers, tailors, and
manufacturers of cardboard boxes'.

5.4.5. Skew isogram. This was discovered by Dr. G. T. Bennett (*Engineering*, 4 Dec. 1903, p. 777). The lengths of alternate links are equal, and the inclinations of the hinges are related by an equation.

We shall give a few special cases in the form of a table, with some additional five-bar chains due to Goldberg (*Trans. Am. Soc. Mech. Eng.* **65** (1943), 649–61).

Author	*No. of bars*	*Length and twist of links*				
Bennett	4	$\begin{cases} 2a \\ 90° \end{cases}$ $\begin{matrix} a \\ 30° \end{matrix}$ $\begin{matrix} 2a \\ 90° \end{matrix}$ $\begin{matrix} a \\ 30° \end{matrix}$				
,,	4	$\begin{cases} a\sqrt{2} \\ 90° \end{cases}$ $\begin{matrix} a \\ 45° \end{matrix}$ $\begin{matrix} a\sqrt{2} \\ 90° \end{matrix}$ $\begin{matrix} a \\ 45° \end{matrix}$				
,,	4	$\begin{cases} a \\ 60° \end{cases}$ $\begin{matrix} a \\ 120° \end{matrix}$ $\begin{matrix} a \\ 60° \end{matrix}$ $\begin{matrix} a \\ 120° \end{matrix}$				
Goldberg	5	$\begin{cases} 2a \\ 90° \end{cases}$ $\begin{matrix} 2a \\ 60° \end{matrix}$ $\begin{matrix} 2a \\ 90° \end{matrix}$ $\begin{matrix} a \\ 30° \end{matrix}$ $\begin{matrix} a \\ 30° \end{matrix}$				
,,	5	$\begin{cases} a(1+\sqrt{2}) \\ 75° \end{cases}$ $\begin{matrix} 2a \\ 90° \end{matrix}$ $\begin{matrix} a\sqrt{2} \\ 45° \end{matrix}$ $\begin{matrix} a \\ 30° \end{matrix}$ $\begin{matrix} 2a \\ 90° \end{matrix}$				

To these must be added the ring of six tetrahedra (3.11) which has a limited mobility. The tetrahedra need not be regular, but must be congruent, with their opposite hinge-edges at right angles. The ring of eight or more tetrahedra will rotate like a smoke-ring.

To construct these chains, it is most convenient to use cardboard tetrahedra for links. To construct a link of length l and twist θ, proceed as follows.

Draw a rectangle with diagonals of length h, the length of a hinge, and containing an angle θ. From a corner of the rectangle drop a perpendicular on to a diagonal, thus dividing it into two parts p and q, the perpendicular being of length x (see Fig. 296). Then the faces of the tetrahedron are triangles whose altitude y is of length $\sqrt{(l^2+x^2)}$, and divides the base into segments p and q. The net of the tetrahedron is shown in Fig. 296.

A further special six-bar chain was discovered by Bricard. It has $\theta = 90°$ throughout, and the lengths of the links are

a, x, b, y, c, z where $a^2+b^2+c^2 = x^2+y^2+z^2$. Integral solutions of these equations can be constructed from the identities:

$$4^2+5^2+20^2 = 8^2+11^2+16^2 = 4^2+13^2+16^2$$
$$= 4^2+8^2+19^2$$
$$= 21^2;$$
$$9^2+12^2+20^2 = 12^2+15^2+16^2 = 25^2.$$

Further examples and references will be found in 'The Freedom of Linkages', *Math. Gazette*, **34** (1950), 37, by R. H. Macmillan.

5.5. MACHINES FOR DRAWING CURVES

5.5.1. Besides the linkages we have discussed, there are other machines designed specially for drawing certain curves. The commonest of these is the ellipsograph, or Trammel of Archimedes, which is used in many drawing offices for constructing ellipses. There are various types in use, but the one which illustrates the principle most clearly is shown diagrammatically in Fig. 297. Four triangular cheek-pieces are bolted firmly to a

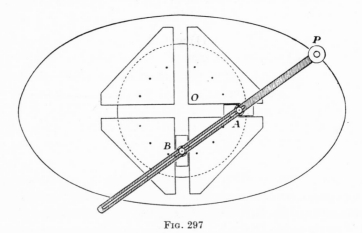

FIG. 297

base-plate which rests on the paper. They form the walls of two slots at right angles in which the sliders A and B can run. PAB is a slotted arm which can be screwed to the sliders at A and B in such a way that it is free to rotate on the slider, but not to slip along the slot AB. The sliders must be longer than the width of the slots at O to ensure free travel across the opening.

If $\widehat{OAB} = \theta$, $BP = a$, $AP = b$, the coordinates of P are $(a\cos\theta, b\sin\theta)$ and the locus of P is the ellipse with axes $2a$ and $2b$. By adjusting the screws, ellipses of different sizes can be drawn by a tracing point at P.

The same apparatus can be used to demonstrate a two-to-one gear ratio, using pins and slots only. The centre O of the base-plate is now fixed, and also the mid-point C of the segment AB of the sliding arm. The distance OC is constant, being equal to $\frac{1}{2}AB$. As the arm is rotated about C, the plate revolves in the opposite sense at one-half the rate. Again, if AB is held fixed and the arm CO is rotated, driving the plate over the sliding contacts at A and B, the fixed point P will cut out an ellipse on any sheet attached to the base plate. This is the principle of *Oldham's Coupling*, by means of which ellipses can be cut on a lathe.

5.5.2. The Archimedean spiral. Another curve which can be drawn with a simple mechanism is the Archimedean spiral $r = a\theta$. A diagram of the mechanism is shown in Fig. 298.

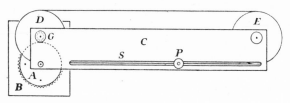

FIG. 298

A is a toothed wheel fixed to the base-plate B. The moving carriage C is free to rotate about the axis of A and carries two pulleys D and E. On the axle of the pulley D, and connected to it, is a small pinion G which meshes with the fixed gear-wheel A. A thread passes round the pulleys D and E and is attached to the tracing-point P which moves in the slot S. Evidently the distance moved by P along the slot is proportional to the angle through which the carriage turns, and the law of the spiral is satisfied.

Q

5.5.3. Lissajous's figures. This is the name given to the family of curves which are described by a point whose motion is the resultant of two simple harmonic motions in perpendicular directions. In general the motions have different periods and amplitudes and a great variety of patterns results. If the periods are equal we obtain various kinds of ellipse; if one period is twice the other, various quartics, with the lemniscate of Bernoulli and the repeated arc of a parabola as special cases.

The curves can be drawn by combining pendulum motions by several different methods, of which Blackburne's pendulum is the example most often given. In this the bob is suspended from the lowest point of three strings knotted in the form of a Y. The upper strings are attached to fixed points. It is clear that the length of the pendulum for motion in the plane of the Y is that of the lower string. For motion perpendicular to this plane the complete Y oscillates about the points of suspension. It is difficult to utilize this to draw a curve on paper, and the range of ratios of the two periods is limited.

For drawing purposes a better method is illustrated in Fig. 299. Two long arms are hinged together and the pen or pencil passes through the centre of the hinge. The far ends of the arms rest on the top of two rods which swing as pendulums in perpendicular planes. The angle between the arms varies, and there is a certain amount of coupling between the motions of the two pendulums, but if the arms are long this is slight and a good approximation to the true Lissajous's figures can be obtained.

The hinge can be a collar of wood, shaped rather like half a small cotton-reel. The pencil must fit tightly in the drill-hole, but the arms must be an easy fit on the outside of the collar. A wooden ring that just fits over the core of the collar can then be glued in place to hold the arms in position. Alternatively, a short length of metal tube can be used, threaded on the outside, with the arms held in place by lock-nuts.

A few curves drawn with a machine of this type are shown in Fig. 300. The ratio given is that of the periods of the two pendulums, and the angle is the approximate initial phase difference between them. Notice in the second figure how the slight

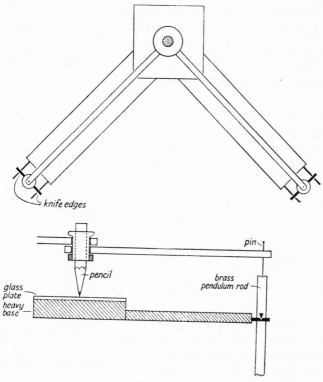

FIG. 299

difference in frequency gradually alters the phase difference, so that the ellipse is reduced ultimately to a straight line. In diagrams 3 and 5, where the initial phase difference is only a few degrees, notice how the coupling between the motions tends to bring them exactly into phase, the loops becoming cusps. It is these slow changes which make the patterns interesting and produce the 'envelopes' which are their most noticeable feature.

The cathode-ray oscillograph also provides a simple method of drawing these curves. The potential difference causing the x-displacement can be derived from 50-cycle mains or a valve-maintained tuning-fork, with a suitable filter to render it sinusoidal. The potential difference for the y-displacement can be obtained from a beat frequency oscillator, which will have a wide range of frequency. The slow changes are easily observed, as the frequencies will not normally be *exact* multiples.

5.5.4. The harmonograph. This machine is an extension of that last described, which combines the motions of two *conical* pendulums. As it is possible to fix these so that they move in perpendicular planes, it is also possible to use this machine to draw Lissajous's figures as a special case. It is however capable of a very wide variety of designs; in fact two patterns drawn by the machine are seldom alike.

The harmonograph was a popular diversion in Victorian drawing-rooms, since when it has suffered a decline and is rarely seen today. The construction of a good machine entails a considerable amount of labour and skill, but the effort will be well repaid, and it makes a fascinating contribution to any mathematical exhibition that may be planned.

To judge from occasional remarks in the literature, the Victorian models were light enough to be placed on a table, and seem to have combined the pendulums one below the other, the second being attached to the bob of the first, and the pen to the lowest bob. What sort of pen was used and how it made contact in all positions with a flat sheet of paper the writer has been unable to discover, but there is no doubt that it produced beautiful and continuous curves. The model described here is of a different

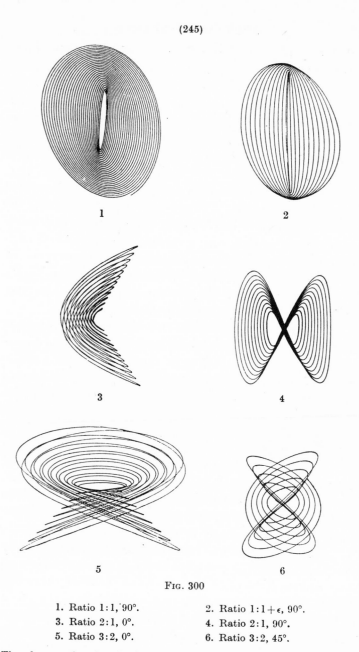

Fig. 300

1. Ratio 1:1, 90°.　　2. Ratio 1:1+ε, 90°.
3. Ratio 2:1, 0°.　　4. Ratio 2:1, 90°.
5. Ratio 3:2, 0°.　　6. Ratio 3:2, 45°.

The phase angles give the fraction of the more rapid period which elapses between the times when the pendulums are at the ends of their paths.

type and much more robust. If the motions are not to decay too rapidly a light pen arm and heavy weights are essential; pendulums about 3 or 4 feet long are also to be recommended.

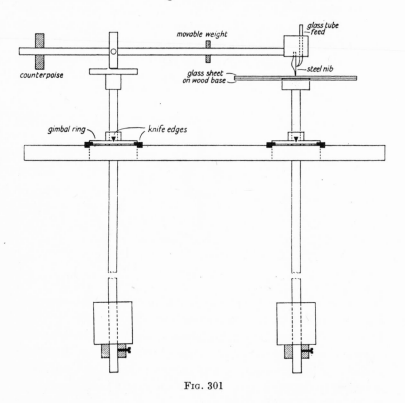

Fig. 301

The principle adopted in this machine is to apply the conical movements separately to the pen and to the table carrying the paper; the pen-arm can then be mounted so as to permit the pen to move up and down, and thus to maintain contact in all positions relative to the table.

Fig. 301 shows a side elevation of the machine. The whole is mounted on a wooden baulk which is securely clamped to rigid supports. (The machine is very sensitive to slight tremors and must be kept as free from vibration as possible.) Two holes about 2-inch diameter and about 1 ft. 6 in. apart are drilled in this baulk. This was done in the model constructed under the writers' direction in order to allow 8-inch amplitude of swing for each pendulum, but in practice the maximum amplitude could not be used owing to the difficulty of finding a pen which would work well at high angles of inclination, so that the distance apart could be reduced to 1 foot with advantage. Brass rings $2\frac{3}{4}$ inches in diameter externally and 2 inches internally were then sunk into the baulk (as shown in the diagram in solid black) to bear

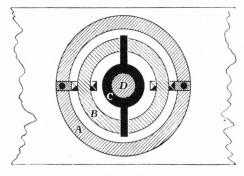

Fig. 302

the steel knife-edges which were bolted to each. This is ring A in Fig. 302. A floating ring B of slightly smaller diameter, grooved to half its depth along one diameter, and again in a similar manner on the opposite side along a perpendicular diameter, rested on these knife-edges, and carried in turn the knife-edges attached to the pendulum. These were inserted in a steel collar C fixed to the brass pendulum rod D. The pendulums, thus supported on gimbals, were free to oscillate in any vertical plane. They were 4 ft. 3 in. long, 3 ft. 6 in. below the knife-edges and 9 inches above, but as this raised the table rather high for comfort the measurements could be reduced. They carried adjustable lead weights, about 10 lb. each, cast in cocoa tins round a central brass tube. These were supported on the pendulums by steel collars with set-screws and could be quickly adjusted to any depth below the knife-edges.

Both pendulums were provided with wooden collars at the top, one of which supported the drawing table, 8 inches square, and the other the pen-arm mounting. A glass plate was clamped to the table to give a smooth writing-surface, and the paper stretched over it with clips. The pen-arm mounting is shown in Fig. 303. The pen-arm was made of angle-section curtain rod laid flat to prevent whipping from side to side, mounted on a horizontal axle which was free to revolve on conical pivots. These were fixed in a brass bridge, also made of curtain rod,

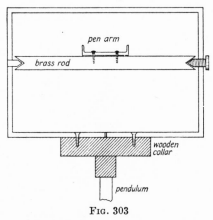

FIG. 303

which was screwed to the collar on the pendulum. This design was adopted to reduce play as much as possible in a horizontal plane, while allowing free vertical motion.

The arm was provided with a counterpoise, and a sliding weight (a large spring paper-clip serves very well) to vary the pressure on the tracing-point or to remove it altogether from contact with the paper. For the construction of the pen, see § 5.5.6.

5.5.5. Twin-elliptic pendulum. The alternative method of applying both conical movements to the table, while keeping the pen-arm fixed except for vertical motion, results in a machine of a different type. In this machine, known as the twin-elliptic pendulum, the table is carried as before on a pendulum, to the lower end of which is attached a second 'deflector' pendulum. The best arrangement is shown in Fig. 304. The pen-arm is now hinged to a fixed support, and its suspension can be lighter and narrower since it moves only up and down. If the table is to be at a convenient height above the floor the pendulums must be

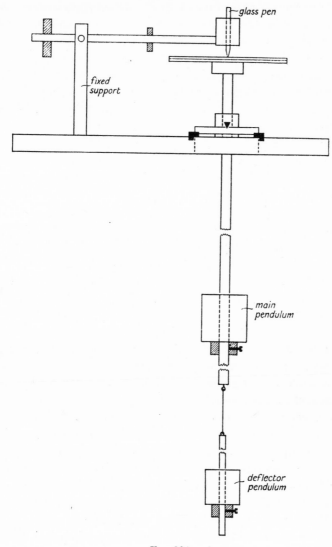

FIG. 304

about half the length of those in Fig. 301. The lower pendulum can consist simply of a thread carrying a heavy bob, and fastened to a hook at the lower end of the main pendulum.

Alternatively, the table (duly weighted) can itself form the bob of the upper pendulum, suspended from gimbals in the roof; the lower pendulum being attached to a hook below the table. A stirrup-shaped suspension of the table is necessary to allow for the fixed pen-arm.

With this arrangement the ratio corresponding to that of the periods of the independent pendulums in the two-pendulum harmonograph is now the ratio of the periods of the *normal vibrations* of the apparatus. These are the two modes of vibration in which the two pendulums remain in a vertical plane which rotates about the vertical axis through the point of suspension. In one, which has the longer period, the bobs are on the same side of this axis. In the other they are on opposite sides. It can be shown that when the ratio is $m:n$ there will be $m+n$ loops or cusps in the resulting curve when the pendulums revolve in opposite directions (*counter-current* motion), and $m-n$ when they revolve in the same direction (*concurrent* motion). The 3:1 ratio is most interesting since it produces symmetrical curves in both cases. This happens whenever m and n are both odd, so that 5:3 is another such case, but frictional damping will be more destructive of the symmetry when m and n are larger.

This machine has different characteristics from the two-pendulum harmonograph. The latter gives some of its best envelopes when the periods are nearly equal, which is impossible for the twin-elliptic machine. On the other hand the twin-elliptic gives better results for high ratios such as 3:1 or 5:2. The ratio can be increased by either raising or lightening the upper weight, or by raising or increasing the lower weight.

It is not easy at first to set a twin-elliptic pendulum in motion in a counter-current manner, but if the 'tuning' of the periods is carefully adjusted beforehand a little practice will enable anyone to start the table moving in the desired figure. This will be like a deltoid for a ratio of 2:1 and an astroid for 3:1, with more complex hypocycloids for other ratios. Full details are given in *Harmonic Vibrations and Vibration Figures*, now, unfortunately, out of print.

Some of the curves actually drawn by machines of these two types are shown in Fig. 305.

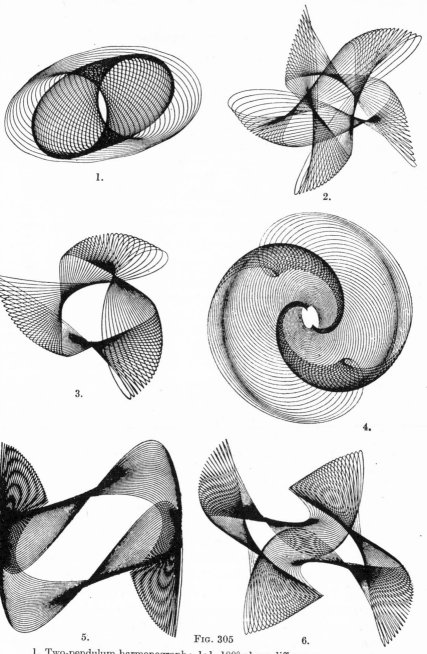

Fig. 305

1. Two-pendulum harmonograph: 1:1, 180° phase difference, concurrent.
2. Two-pendulum harmonograph: 3:2, counter-current.
3. Twin-elliptic pendulum: 2:1, counter-current.
4. Twin-elliptic pendulum: 3– :1, concurrent.
5. Twin-elliptic pendulum: 3– :1, concurrent, deflexion almost linear.
6. Twin-elliptic pendulum: 3:1, counter-current.

5.5.6. Construction of pens. The pen used in either type of harmonograph can be either a steel nib provided with a glass feed-tube, as shown in Fig. 301, or a glass pen as shown in Fig. 304. A ball-pointed pen requires too much pressure. The steel nib and feed-tube can be conveniently mounted in holes drilled through a cube of wood which is attached to the pen-

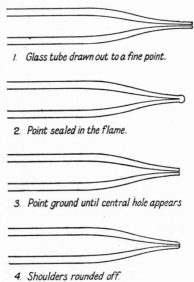

1. Glass tube drawn out to a fine point.

2. Point sealed in the flame.

3. Point ground until central hole appears

4. Shoulders rounded off.

Fig. 306. Stages in the manufacture of a glass pen.

arm. The single glass pen can be similarly supported, or merely held in a spring clip of wire.

The glass pen, if well made, works more smoothly than the steel nib, but it will not usually draw such fine lines, and a quick-drying ink may be necessary to avoid smudging the pattern.

To make a glass pen, take a length of fine glass tubing—standard wall tubing 4 to 6 mm. in diameter is best, not capillary tubing—and heat it evenly at the centre in a gas flame. Draw out the tube rapidly and separate the two halves, thus obtaining two narrow drawn-out tubes as in Fig. 306 (1). These will be too brittle for use as they are. To strengthen them, seal off the ends at a point where the glass walls are not too fine (Fig. 306 (2)). With carborundum paste, obtainable from a repair garage, carefully grind down the sealed end of each tube until the tiniest central hole appears (Fig. 306 (3)). The grinding should be done on a glass plate with the pen held at right angles to it. Finally, with a rolling action, holding the pen at an acute angle with the plate, grind the shoulders smooth so that the pen has an even, rounded point (Fig. 306 (4)). The line drawn on the paper will be the full width of the pen-point, not merely the diameter of the hole.

To fill the pen with ink, suck it up through the point, as in a pipette. By this means particles large enough to clog the pen are excluded. If the ink dries in the pen and clogs it, concentrated nitric acid will usually free it. Always wash out the pen with clean water after use, and keep it in a beaker of water.

An expensive, but more durable alternative, is to use a 'Rapidograph' drawing pen with a fine bore, 0·2 or 0·3 mm.

Any writing-ink may be used, including coloured inks, but not of course fixed Indian ink. For a quick-drying ink, 'Indurite' or hectograph ink may be recommended. A good bond writing-paper is best, or, for more permanent work, a smooth thin pasteboard. Highly-glazed 'art' paper, loaded with china clay, should not be used, as the filling quickly clogs the pen.

5.5.7. Meccanograph. A machine somewhat similar to the harmonograph was described some years ago in the literature supplied with Meccano sets. A table, made to oscillate in a horizontal straight line by means of an eccentric drive from a rotating shaft, carries the pivot of a pen-arm which is deflected from side to side by another cam geared to the same shaft. The pen carried by this arm traced the resulting curve on a rotating table, driven by a worm-gear from the same motor as the rest of the machine. By altering the position of the pivot, the throws of the cams, and the gear ratios, many interesting and repeatable patterns can be obtained of epicyclic type. From a mathematical point of view however they are somewhat artificial, and their equations are complicated. If the table does not rotate, curves approximating to Lissajous's figures are described. A full description of the machine is given on p. 61 of the current *Meccano Manual* for Sets 7 and 8.

MODELS FOR LOGIC AND COMPUTING

THERE have been many attempts to make a machine which will solve simple logical problems, such as the following:

'Mary will not serve on the Social Committee if Susan is on it. John will only serve if Mary does. One of the girls must be on the Committee. What combinations of these three candidates are possible?'

Most people will solve this readily in their heads, but in more complicated problems a mechanical procedure may be helpful. To see how simple cases can be solved mechanically assists in understanding more elaborate machines; we shall therefore outline a method by which this can be done.

6.1. LOGICAL DEVICES

6.1.1. The propositional calculus

We begin by describing a symbolism which is a useful shorthand. We let single letters $p, q,...$ stand for *statements*, or propositions which may be *true* or *false*. If p is true, we say p has the *value* 1; if p is false, the *value* 0. For example, in the above problem we could put m for the statement 'Mary is on the committee', and so on. Propositions can be related by *logical connectives*. We write $p.q$ for the compound statement 'p and q'; $p.q$ is true if and only if both p and q are true. The value of $p.q$ is the product of the values of p and q. We write $p \vee q$ for the compound statement 'p or q (or both)'. $p \vee q$ is false if and only if both p and q are false. We write $p \Rightarrow q$ for the statement 'if p, then q'. This means p cannot be true and q false, so either p is false or q is true, or both: i.e. 'not-p, or q'. If two statements p, q are true or false together we write $p \equiv q$ ('p is equivalent to q'). If we write $\sim p$ for 'not-p' we can say $(p \Rightarrow q) \equiv (\sim p \vee q)$ The reader can verify *De Morgan's Rules*:

$$\sim(p \vee q) \equiv (\sim p).(\sim q)$$
$$\sim(p.q) \equiv (\sim p) \vee (\sim q).$$

The values of these and other *functions* of p and q are conveniently exhibited in a *truth-table*; this gives the value of each function corresponding to the four possible combinations of values of p and q.

p	q	$\sim p$	$\sim q$	$p.q$	$p \vee q$	$p \Rightarrow q$	$p \equiv q$	$p \not\equiv q$	$p \mid q$
1	1	0	0	1	1	1	1	0	0
1	0	0	1	0	1	0	0	1	1
0	1	1	0	0	1	1	0	1	1
0	0	1	1	0	0	1	1	0	1

Thus $p \mid q$ ('p stroke q') means 'not both p and q', or, by de Morgan's rule, 'not-p, or not-q (or both)'. An example should make the meaning of the table clear. The '1' in the second row of the last column but one means that $p \not\equiv q$ is *true* if p is true and q is false; i.e. that in that case 'p is not the same as q'.

We can now state our committee problem in the form

$$(s \Rightarrow \sim m).(j \Rightarrow m).(s \vee m),$$

and we wish to find the values of s, m, and j for which this function has the value 1. We can do this by constructing the complete truth-table for the eight possible combinations of s, m, and j. This, in fact, is how most simple logical machines work. Alternatively we can develop an algebra for dealing with the values of such expressions. We shall not develop this here, since our object is to describe models, not to write a treatise on propositional calculus. The interested reader can refer to books in the bibliography. This particular problem, however, can be quickly solved by noting that

$$(s \Rightarrow \sim m) \equiv \sim s \vee \sim m; \qquad (\sim s \vee \sim m).(s \vee m) \equiv (s \not\equiv m).$$

Combining this with $(j \Rightarrow m)$ gives $j.m$, m, and s as the only possible combinations. This is merely putting in symbols the argument which most people would use.

6.1.2. Venn diagrams. Relations between propositions can be illustrated in a simple way. We can regard a proposition p as a way of *selecting* from the objects under discussion those for which p is true. Thus m selects the committees which include Mary. We represent this selection by the inside of a closed area

$a.b$ is then represented by the area *common* to the two areas a and b; $a \vee b$ by the area included in either or both. These areas are shaded in the diagrams shown (Fig. 307). In practice it is

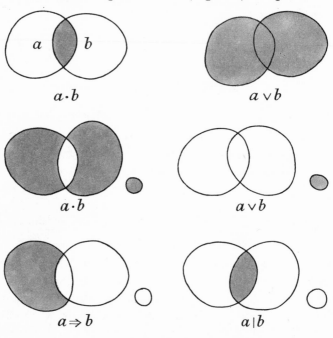

Fig. 308

usually better to shade the areas for which the statement is *not* true; to save shading all the paper for $\sim a \cdot \sim b$ we draw an extra small circle to represent everything outside the a and b circles. Our diagram is now as shown in Fig. 308, and one or two other examples are given. The shading *excludes* the regions inconsistent with the truth of the proposition.

6.1.3. Window reading cards. The way to solve our problem is now clear. We must design cards to correspond to the various Venn diagrams, with holes cut where the circles are *unshaded*. We need a card for each compound statement. We then superpose the cards and the solution appears through all the cards. For our problem, suitable cards would be as shown (Fig. 309):

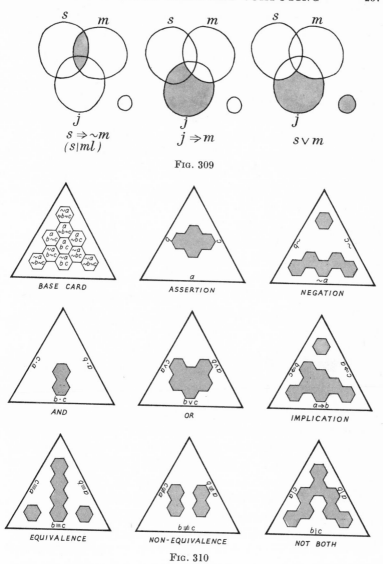

Fig. 309

Fig. 310

If the unshaded areas are cut away and the cards superposed, it will be found that there is clear daylight through the areas for $j.m.\sim s$, $\sim j.m.\sim s$, and $\sim j.\sim m.s$, which are the three solutions.

It is obviously wasteful to cut separate cards for every problem. What we want is a standard set, and preferably one in
which each card can be turned round, so that one and the same
card can be used for $a \Rightarrow b$, $b \Rightarrow c$, and $c \Rightarrow a$. Also circles are
awkward to cut out. A set of this kind using hexagons is given
in the diagram, and is a modification of a system devised by
Martin Gardner of *The Scientific American*. The first card is a
base card, and is laid down first. The others have the shaded
areas cut out; they are turned so that the appropriate statement
appears at the bottom and are placed in any order on the base.
Possible true combinations appear through the windows. The
sixth card can be turned over to give $b \Rightarrow a$ and so on; the others
are symmetrical.

6.2. Punched Cards

We can also solve problems of the same type with a set of
punched cards. For our problem with three propositions we
need 2^3 or 8 cards, each with three holes punched near the top
edge. The diagram shows a typical card for three propositions
a, b, and c (Fig. 311).

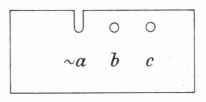

Fig. 311

This particular card represents the situation $\sim a.b.c$; i.e. a is
false, while b and c are true. It will be seen that $\sim a$ is represented by cutting a slot into the hole a; when a needle is inserted
into the hole a, the card will not be lifted with the needle but
will drop. Eight cards are prepared, one for each possible
combination of holes and slots. The cards for which $a \vee b$ is true
can be selected by pushing two needles through the holes for a
and b simultaneously and lifting; the required cards will rise.
Those for which $a.b$ is true can be selected by two operations;

put the needle in a and lift and take the cards that rise; then put the needle in hole b in these cards, and lift again. In practice the cards should be stood upright in a wide box, and knitting-needles can be used with great facility. The system obviously extends easily to any number of propositions.

To solve our problem, we let a, b, c now stand for 'John is on the committee', 'Mary is on', and 'Susan is on'. We have to combine the statements $a \Rightarrow b$, $b \mid c$, $b \vee c$. The third statement is the simplest; let us deal with it first. To do this we take two needles and pass them through the b and c holes. Then we lift, and those that have holes at b or c will rise. We take these and pass to the first statement. Because of the way the cards are made, we cannot deal with a $\vee$-operation with negatives in this way. Instead we need two operations. Thus, to deal with the first statement, we write it as $\sim a \vee b$. We spear a and take the cards that *drop* (i.e. those that have $\sim a$). Then we take the remaining cards, spear b, take those that *rise* and put them with the first group. Now we take these and use the second state-ment. Here we spear b and c in turn and take the cards which *drop* each time. We are left with three cards: $a, b, \sim c$; $\sim a, b, \sim c$; $\sim a, \sim b, c$; giving John and Mary but not Susan; Mary only; Susan only. The procedure is not nearly so complicated to carry out as it is to describe.

6.2.1. The binary scale. This system of slotting the cards is, of course, equivalent to numbering them in the binary scale. It is convenient to regard a hole as representing a zero digit, and a slot as representing a unit. The card pictured above would have the binary 'code-number' 100; if we regard these digits as written in the normal order, with the least significant digit on the right, this is the binary representation of the number 4. If we have a set of 64 cards, for example, we can number them from 0 to 63 in the binary scale with 6 digits. For example, card number 27 will have the digits 011011, standing for

$$0 \times 2^5 + 1 \times 2^4 + 1 \times 2^3 + 0 \times 2^2 + 1 \times 2 + 1.$$

Now cut slots in the cards for the 1-digits. Card number 27 appears as shown below (Fig. 312).

This card can be picked out at once from the pack of 64. First of all we push a needle through holes 1 and 4 (from the left) in turn and lift; then, taking the cards that rise, we spear four needles through holes 2, 3, 5, 6; our card alone will be let fall. The pack

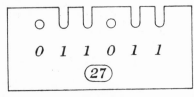

0   1   1   0   1   1

27

Fig. 312

demonstrates another remarkable fact; however it is shuffled it can be restored to numerical order by six operations. Spear each hole in turn, beginning at the right, and bring the cards lifted by the needle to the front.

Many logical problems can be solved with such a pack of cards. Plain card-index cards can be used; an ordinary paper-punch will punch the holes and then the slots can be cut out with scissors. A good deal of play is advisable in the box in which the cards are stacked, or they will not separate easily.

6.3. Electric Circuits

So far our models have been mere toys, though the last is useful in making catalogues that have to be sorted into alphabetical order. But if we translate the binary coding into electrical circuits we are on the main road that leads to the modern electronic computer.

We begin with a simple logical machine. If our propositions a and $\sim a$ are represented by two-position switches, we can make a mean 'the switch A is *on*', and $\sim a$ 'the switch A is *off*'. Logical connectives between a and b can be shown by wiring between switches A and B; for $a \vee b$ we put A and B in parallel (Fig. 313); if either switch is switched on, current will flow. For $a.b$ we put A and B in series (Fig. 314); both switches must now be on for current to pass.

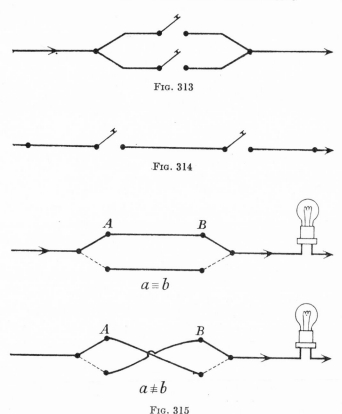

FIG. 313

FIG. 314

$a \equiv b$

$a \not\equiv b$

FIG. 315

For other connectives we need two-way switches which show both a and $\sim a$. The ordinary two-way staircase switch is either an $a \equiv b$ or an $a \not\equiv b$ circuit according to how it is wired (see Fig. 315).

6.3.1. A simple logical machine. To build the machine, we need three three-pole two-way switches for A, B, and C. Rotary radio-type switches are very convenient. We also need to connect them in various ways in accordance with the given statements. To do this we must set up a socket board with a row of sockets for each statement, labelled A, a, $\sim a$; B, b, $\sim b$; C, c, $\sim c$. The A's are connected to the three poles of switch A, by permanent wiring; the a's to one set of corresponding output contacts of the switch, and the $\sim a$'s to the other, as in Fig. 316. (The suffixes refer to the rows of sockets.)

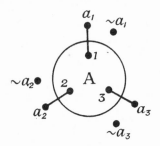

FIG. 316

Similarly for B and C.

Wiring for the connectives is alterable; short leads with plugs at each end should be plugged into the sockets in accordance with the schemes shown (Fig. 317). The reader can easily devise

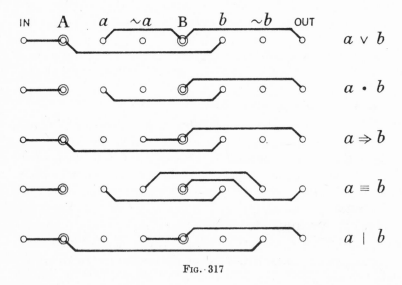

FIG. 317

schemes for any other connectives that may be wanted. The ingenious can construct permanent set-ups of plugs on a short strip for each connective which is required, or standard octal valve-base sockets and plugs can be used.

A sketch of a complete machine is shown in Fig. 318, set up for the problem at the beginning of the chapter.

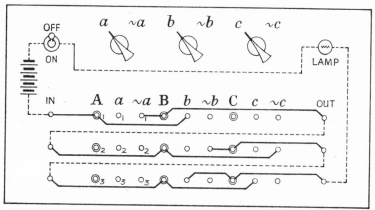

FIG. 318. ——— Plug connexions; - - - - hidden connexions (connexions to three-pole switches not shown). Machine set up for the problem

$$(a \Rightarrow b).(b\,|\,c).(b \vee c)$$

To operate the machine, switch on, and systematically run through all the positions of switches A, B, and C. The simplest way to do this is to use the scheme of changes $ABACABA$ where each letter indicates a reversal of the corresponding switch. Note the combinations for which the lamp lights up. They are the solutions of the problem.

The machine can obviously be extended indefinitely, but the process of 'scanning' the entire truth-table by setting the switches becomes tedious.

6.4. BINARY ADDITION

If we add two binary digits a and b, the sum digit and the carry digit are seen in the following table:

		a			a	
SUM	0	1	CARRY	0	1
	0	0	1		0	0	0
b				b		
	1	1	0		1	0	1

In logical terms, the sum is the *value of a* $\not\equiv b$, the *carry* that of $a.b$. A circuit to do this is easily devised. We need two-pole two-way switches for a and b; the wiring is shown in the diagram. (The switches are all shown in the '0' position.) The right half of Fig. 319 is the circuit for the 'carry' digit. Current will pass along the line c_1 when both a and b are 1; i.e. c_1 gives the 'carry' digit $a.b$. But in addition a circuit is provided to carry 0, giving current in c_0 when either a or b (or both) is 0; i.e. c_0 gives $a \mid b$. The necessity for the c_0 line will appear later.

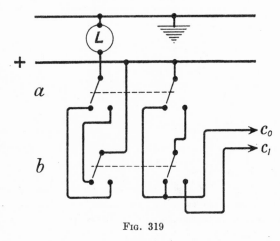

FIG. 319

Fig. 319 thus shows a complete unit for adding two single binary digits, 'putting down' the sum in the light L and 'carrying' 0 or 1 to c_0 or c_1 respectively. Such a device is called a *half-adder*.

Except at the least significant end of two binary numbers which are to be added, there are *three* possible digits which have to be added at each stage, since there may be a 'carry in' digit as well as the two digits in the binary numbers; e.g. in the sum

$$\begin{array}{r} 111 \\ 110 \\ \hline 1101 \end{array}$$

the third column from the right (the 'fours' column) contains the addition of two 1's and a carry of 1 from the twos column. To effect this without the use of rectifiers four-pole switches are needed, as shown in Fig. 320, though other arrangements are possible. The left-hand side of this diagram caters for the 'put down' figure indicated by the light; the rest deals with the 'carry out' to the next column. Note that these diagrams are shown from the underneath or wiring side of the machine, so that the

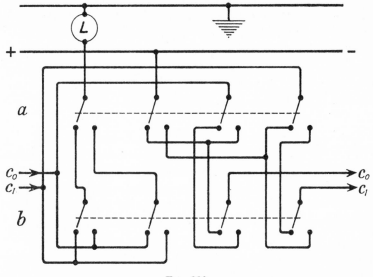

Fig. 320

least significant digit is on the *left*. On the upper (switch) side the digits will be in conventional order.

It is now clear why a c_0 line is required, for we need to bring up power to each stage even if there is 0 to carry. Power injected separately at each stage could get back down the c_1 line to earlier stages unless rectifiers were included. Power has to be injected for the same reason to operate the outgoing c_0 line when the a and b digits are both zero, since otherwise there would have to be a connexion in this condition between the ingoing c_0 and c_1 lines which would allow current to get back into the previous stage.

To add two numbers from 0 to 15, four binary digits are needed in each number and five in the answer. The least significant digit requires a half-adder (Fig. 319), the remainder full adders; except that the most significant full adder needs no c_0 carry-out line and it will be found that two three-pole switches suffice with a minor rearrangement. Therefore for each number we need one two-pole, one three-pole, and two four-pole two-way switches, five flash-bulbs for displaying the answer—the final one connected of course to the outgoing c_1 line—a simple chassis and a battery.

Although an enterprising amateur can build for himself some of the circuits actually found in a big electronic computer and experiment with valves and transistors, the ideas and difficulties involved belong rather to Physics than to Mathematics or Logic, and we cannot enter upon them here.

6.5. ANALOGUE COMPUTERS

A digital computer operates with digits, usually binary, which are either 1 or 0. They are represented by various physical devices which are in one or other of two states—roughly speaking, either 'on' or 'off'. An analogue computer, however, represents numbers by physical quantities and operates on them physically, not logically. These quantities may be voltages, resistances, distances, rotations, or a variety of things; they will ultimately be read on a scale of some kind. We have only space for a few.

6.5.1. The Wheatstone bridge. The Wheatstone bridge circuit is, of course, a simple device for multiplication and division. In the position of balance when no current flows through the galvanometer G, $R_1 R_4 = R_2 R_3$. The bridge is customarily used to find unknown resistances, but if we use it with known and calibrated resistances, it becomes a computing device. The metre bridge can of course be used for accurate work, but for demonstration R_1, R_2, R_3, and R_4 may be wirewound linear potentiometers of the radio type, with rotary knobs reading on calibrated dials. Simple scales suffice to find products: set R_1 to a convenient unit and $R_4 = R_2 \times R_3$; or quotients: $R_2 = R_4 \div R_3$. If the dials are calibrated logarithmically for R_3 and R_4, the bridge can be used to evaluate powers and roots. Suppose the reading of R_3's knob is r_3, where $\log r_3 = R_3$, and the same for R_4, while R_1 and R_2 read linearly as usual. Then the balance condition is $R_1 \log r_4 = R_2 \log r_3$ or

$r_4^{R_1} = r_3^{R_2}$; r_4 therefore reads the value of $r_3^{R_2/R_1}$. A wide variety of simple calculations can thus be carried out; for example we may solve triangles by using a scale such that $\sin r_3 = R_3$, with r_3 reading directly in degrees, and the same for r_4; then $R_1 : R_2$ is the ratio of the sides of a triangle opposite angles r_3 and r_4.

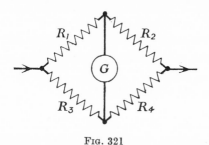

FIG. 321

6.5.2. The high-gain amplifier.

In this analogue computer the physical quantity which represents the number is a voltage. The high-gain amplifier can be thought of as a device for maintaining a voltage at very small levels at the input end—e.g. on the grid of the first valve—while magnifying its changes into very large voltages at the output end. The fundamental circuits are shown in the diagrams. In the first circuit (Fig. 322 a) there is positive feedback through a resistance R_0, the current in which is $V_o(1+1/m)/R_0$ which must be the same as $\{-V_i-V_o/m\}/R_i$, neglecting grid current. Therefore, if m is large, we have effectively $V_o R_i + V_i R_0 = 0$. In the second arrangement (Fig. 322 b) with capacitative feedback, we have

$$\left\{-V_i-\frac{V_o}{m}\right\}\Big/R_i = C\,\frac{d}{dt}\left\{V_o\left(1+\frac{1}{m}\right)\right\},$$

or, effectively, $\qquad R_i C\dfrac{dV_o}{dt}+V_i = 0.$

The two circuits thus perform the operations of addition and integration respectively. Units of these types can therefore be coupled together to give linear or linear differential equations and the output voltages can be read off directly with a voltmeter or on a cathode-ray oscilloscope as functions of the time for fixed or varying input voltages. The actual circuitry involves

(268)

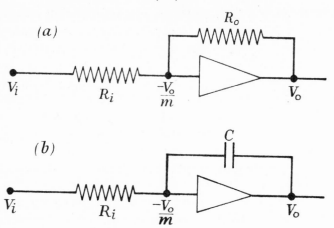

denotes a high-gain amplifier with voltage amplification factor m.

Fig. 322

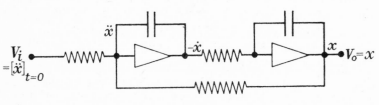

Fig. 323

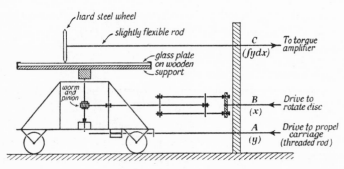

Fig. 324

a number of technical problems, but experimental computers suitable for 'do-it-yourself' techniques have been set up at the Cambridge University Engineering Laboratory and at the Department of Electronics at Southampton University. Commercial units for amateur assembly are available (at high prices) in the U.S.A. A diagram of the set-up for the equation $\ddot{x} + n^2 x = 0$ is shown in Fig. 323. Further information can be found in B. H. Venning, 'Analogue computers as an aid to teaching', *Bulletin of Elec. Eng. Education*, Dec. 1958.

6.5.3. The Bush differential analyser. A full account of this machine was given by Professor Hartree in *Math. Gazette*, **22** (1938), 342. No machine was more inappropriately named, for although the machine will carry out Fourier analysis, its essential function is integration and its method is fundamentally synthetic.

The essential part of the machine is the integrating unit, which consists of a circular disk, rotating in a horizontal plane about a vertical axle, on which rests a small wheel at the end of a horizontal axle, the two forming a variable gear (see Fig. 324). Either the disk or the wheel must be capable of horizontal motion, usually the disk, as the wheel must be coupled to a torque amplifier (see below).

When the wheel is y' units from the centre of the disk, and the disk rotates through an angle dx' radians, the wheel turns through an angle $Ky'\,dx'$, where K is a constant factor. The displacement y' of the disk is effected by rotation of a screw-threaded rod A; the rotation dx' is obtained through a worm or bevel gear from another rod B; and the small wheel rotates, through the torque amplifiers, a third rod C. If y is the total rotation of rod A, at the instant when the rod B has turned through x revolutions, then the rod C will have made $\lambda \int_0^x y\,dx$ turns, where λ is a constant factor depending on the various gear ratios and pitches of the screws. Suppose the rod B is rotated by a motor, which also drives a platform uniformly across a graph $y = f(x)$ in the direction of the x-axis (see Fig. 325), while a screwed rod D, operated by hand, keeps a pointer always on the curve; then if D is geared to the rod A, the area will be measured on a suitable scale by the number of turns made by C.

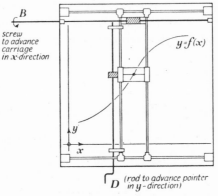

Fig. 325

This is the straightforward use of the machine as an integrator. But by coupling one integrating unit to another in various ways we can use it to solve differential equations. As an example, let us take $\dfrac{d^2y}{dx^2} = -ky$. We can write this in the form $z = \int y \, dx$, $-y = k \int z \, dx$. Let us call the rods of one integrator A_1, B_1, C_1 as before, and the corresponding rods of a second integrator A_2, B_2, and C_2. Now suppose a motor drives B_1 and B_2 at the same rate, dx/dt. If y is the rotation of A_1, that of C_1 will be z on a suitable scale. We therefore use C_1 to drive A_2, through a gear train, with ratio r_1, say. C_2 then generates y by its rotation, and can be used to drive A_1 through another gear train with ratio $-r_2$ (i.e. with a reversal of sense).

We then have $z_1 = \lambda_1 \int y_1 \, dx$, $y_2 = \lambda_2 \int z_2 \, dx$, $z_2 = r_1 z_1$, $y_1 = -r_2 y_2$; the suffixes referring to the corresponding integrators. Finally

$$\frac{dy_2}{dx} = \lambda_2 z_2 = \lambda_2 r_1 z_1 = \lambda_2 r_1 \lambda_1 \int y_1 \, dx, \quad \frac{d^2y_2}{dx^2} = -(\lambda_1 \lambda_2 r_1 r_2)y_2,$$

so that by suitable choice of gear ratios the equation is solved. y_2 can be drawn as a function of x by the same method as before (Fig. 325); B is driven by the motor and D by the rod C_2. The initial conditions are the values of y and $z = \dfrac{dy}{dx}$ when $x = 0$; they are fixed by the positions of the carriages at the start. If the gear-ratios and initial conditions are chosen so that if $\lambda_1 \lambda_2 r_1 r_2 = n^2$, $y = A \sin nx$ and $z = A \cos nx$, then, if y is made to drive the rod D and z the rod B, the pointer will describe a circle.

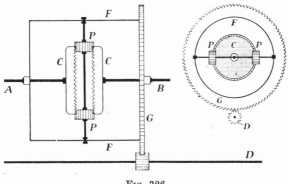

Fig. 326

The only other element of the machine necessary to solve simple integral equations is the adding unit, which adds together the rotations of two rods. This is shown diagrammatically in Fig. 326, and resembles a differential on a motor-car. The pinions P rotate freely on the axle which is carried by the frame F bolted to the gear-wheel G. This is driven by a pinion on the rod D. The spindles A and B rotate freely in the frame F, and are attached to crown-wheels C, which engage the pinions P. Then the rotation of A+the rotation of B = twice the rotation of G. Multiplication by a constant factor can be effected by gearing; multiplication of two variables requires the use of an integrator.

The main technical difficulties in the construction of the machine are the integrating plate and the wheel, and the torque amplifiers. The disk must be accurately plane; a sheet of glass mounted on a rigid support does very well, or a sheet of plastic. For the wheel a hard steel wheel should be used with its rim ground to a bevelled edge. If the spindle on which the wheel is mounted is sufficiently long, it will be flexible enough to ensure adequate pressure between wheel and disk; if necessary, however, a universal joint can be inserted in it.

The drive from the steel wheel is very feeble, and has to be boosted by a torque amplifier. This is shown diagrammatically in Fig. 327. A and B are two highly polished drums attached to

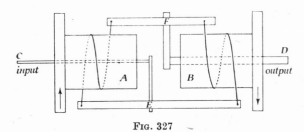

FIG. 327

pulleys which idle on the shafts C and D. C is the shaft from the integrating wheel, and to it is attached by a crank a short arm E. D is the output shaft, which will normally be the input shaft of a second stage of amplification; two stages are usually necessary and sufficient. The output shaft of the second stage is coupled to the rest of the machine. The shaft D carries a crank bearing a similar arm F. E and F are connected by cables of narrow tape or gut which are wound two or three times in opposite senses around the drums. The drums are rotated at high speed by an electric motor, again in opposite senses as indicated. If C rotates so that E moves into the paper, the cable on B will tighten and the rotating drum will pull F over until it becomes slack again. If C rotates in the opposite direction drum A comes into play. The drums must be kept highly polished and lubricated with talc or graphite; otherwise the amplifier may 'hunt', or seize up altogether with disastrous consequences. Apart from these items, a model can be made of standard Meccano parts. The chief inaccuracies arise from backlash, which should be reduced to a minimum; spring-loading the gears is a help, but in a full-scale machine special steps are taken to overcome it.

6.5.4. The Amsler polar planimeter. This is undoubtedly the simplest and most practicable of the integrators. It is reasonably common in the offices of estate agents from which it may be possible to borrow a model for examination. As the machine really works by a difference method, it has to be very accurately made to get good results. Nevertheless, the principle can be demonstrated by a home-made model without difficulty.

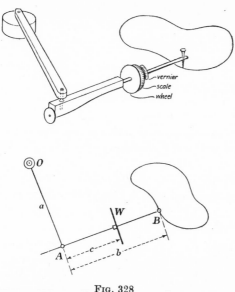

FIG. 328

The instrument consists of two rods OA, AB hinged together at A (Fig. 328). The point O is kept fixed (by a pin through the rod pressed into the drawing board), and at B is a pointer which is carried round the perimeter of the area required. The rod AB carries a wheel W with a bevelled edge which rotates when the rod moves perpendicular to itself but slips when it moves in its own direction. The angle turned through by the wheel is proportional to the area, which can therefore be read off from a scale attached to the wheel and suitably calibrated. In fact, the area swept out by B if A returns to its original position $= AB \times$ distance rolled by wheel. If A completes a circuit of O, a constant area, $\pi(a^2 - 2bc + b^2)$, must be added to the reading of the wheel. In commercial machines the wheel is usually carried on a side axle mounted in very accurately aligned bearings, or else on an extra spindle behind the hinge A. The hinge itself is sometimes a ball-and-cone arrangement; a vertical pin with a spherical end on the rod OA rests in a conical hole drilled in the rod AB.

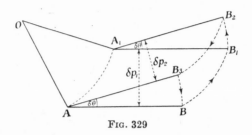

FIG. 329

The fundamental principle of the instrument can be proved either by integration, or as follows. Let the point B undergo the following cycle of movements (Fig. 329).

(1) Rotate OA to OA_1 and let AB move parallel to itself to A_1B_1. Then the area swept out by $AB = b\,\delta p_1$, where $b = AB$, and δp_1 = distance rolled by W = distance between AB and A_1B_1.

(2) Rotate A_1B_1 about A_1 to A_1B_2; W rotates through an angle $\delta\theta$.

(3) Rotate OA_1 back to OA, A_1B_1 moving parallel to itself to AB_3. Area swept out by $AB = b\,\delta p_2$.

(4) Rotate AB_3 into its original position AB. W rotates through an angle $-\delta\theta$, cancelling out the effect of operation (2).

Thus the area $BB_1B_2B_3 = b(\delta p_1 - \delta p_2) = b \times$ distance rolled by W. Since any area can be supposed divided into elementary curvilinear parallelograms of this type, the result is general. If the angle OAB is held rigid, and B describes a complete circle about O, then if $O\widehat{A}B = \alpha$, $O\widehat{W}A = \beta$, $OW = x$ (Fig. 330),

area swept out by $B = \pi(a^2 + b^2 - 2ab\cos\alpha)$.

But the reading of the wheel $= b \times$ distance rolled by wheel
$$= b \times 2\pi x \cos\beta,$$

since the tangent to the path of W makes a constant angle β with the normal to the rod AB.

Therefore the excess of the area swept out over the reading of the wheel

$$= \pi(a^2+b^2-2ab\cos\alpha)-2\pi bx\cos\beta$$
$$= \pi(a^2+b^2)-2\pi b(a\cos\alpha+x\cos\beta)$$
$$= \pi(a^2+b^2-2bc).$$

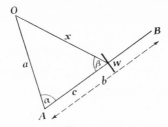

FIG. 330

6.5.5. The slide-rule.

The ordinary slide-rule is a simple form of analogue computer, the physical quantity used to represent numbers being length. The rule is very familiar, and is the subject of a specialized literature, so that no description need be given. It is, however, instructive to make a simple logarithmic rule from first principles, and this is easily done.

The material used can be card, for a small rule, or plywood for a large demonstration model. Such a rule can be 5 or 6 feet long if desired and considerable accuracy can then be obtained. The tongue and groove are best made by gluing slightly over-lapping strips of card or plywood together: the groove should be made slightly wider than the tongue.

It is, of course, possible to graduate the rule by simple reference to the logarithm tables. It is much more interesting, however, to build up the graduations from scratch, using only the basic principle of the rule, that addition of lengths is to correspond to multiplication of the inscribed numbers. The first thing to do is to place the number 2 accurately on the rule. In what follows let us write $d(x)$ for the distance from the graduation 1 to the graduation x. By the fundamental principle, $10d(2) = d(1024) = 3d(10)+d(1\cdot024)$. The last distance is obviously small, and if we neglect it we find that $d(2) = 0\cdot3\times d(10)$. This is quite good enough for a simple rule, in which we can make $d(10) = 5$ inches and $d(2) = 1\cdot5$ inches, but greater accuracy can easily be obtained. All that is necessary is to multiply $1 \cdot 01$ by itself 25 times. This is a labour, but it gives us all we need for a really accurate rule. If this is done, we find that $25d(1 \cdot 01) = d(1 \cdot 2824) \doteq 7d(2) - 2d(10)$. It is also obvious that $d(1 \cdot 024) = 2 \cdot 4 \times d(1 \cdot 01)$ very nearly, so that we now have two simultaneous equations for the ratios of $d(2)$, $d(10)$, and $d(1 \cdot 01)$, namely

$$10d(2) - 3d(10) = 2 \cdot 4d(1 \cdot 01),$$
$$7d(2) - 2d(10) = 25d(1 \cdot 01).$$

Solving these in the ordinary way gives $d(2)/d(10) = 0 \cdot 30103$, and $d(1 \cdot 01)/d(10) = 0 \cdot 0043$, which agree with the true values to four decimal places.

With 1, 2, 10, and $1 \cdot 01$ placed on the rule, we can use the rule itself in the normal way to place 5, 4, 8, $1 \cdot 6$, $2 \cdot 5$, $3 \cdot 2$, and so on. To place 3, we can use $4d(3) = d(81) = d(8) + d(10) + d(1 \cdot 0125)$, and approximate to the last term by the value

$$0 \cdot 0043 \times 1 \cdot 0125 \times d(10) = d(10) \times 0 \cdot 0044.$$

This gives $d(3)/d(10) = 0 \cdot 477$. 3, 6, and 9 can now be placed on the rule, followed by $1 \cdot 2$, $1 \cdot 5$, $1 \cdot 8$, $2 \cdot 4$, $2 \cdot 7$, $3 \cdot 6$, $4 \cdot 5$, $4 \cdot 8$, $5 \cdot 4$, $7 \cdot 2$, $7 \cdot 5$, $8 \cdot 1$, and $9 \cdot 6$. We can place 7 either by estimating the position of $4 \cdot 9$ or by using the more accurate equation

$$4d(7) = d(2401) = d(2 \cdot 4) + 3d(10) + 0 \cdot 0002d(10),$$

the small correction being obtained as $d(1 \cdot 01)/24$.

A very little further work now suffices to locate all the first decimal place divisions from $1 \cdot 1$ to $9 \cdot 9$ with at least three-place accuracy, making judicious use of interpolation by means of our table of powers of $1 \cdot 01$. It will be sufficiently accurate for most purposes if the second decimal places are now filled in by uniform division of the distances for the tenths.

Once the basic scale is constructed, there is no difficulty in adding the refinement of a half-length scale for squares and square-roots, as on the standard rule.

It should also be mentioned that graph-paper logarithmically divided is available commercially, and strips cut from such paper and stuck on card can also be used to make a rule.

The first marking out is best done in pencil; when the divisions have been accurately located and checked they can be scribed or painted and varnished.

6.5.6. Other uses of the slide-rule principle. The method of construction outlined in the preceding paragraph generates a scale in which $d(x) = k \log_{10} x$. But this is by no means the only use for the sliding rule. If we divide the fixed rule in this way, but graduate the slide so that $d(y) = k \log \sin y°$, then the rule can be used directly to solve triangles by means of the sine formula. We have only to bring the graduation on the x-scale corresponding to one of the sides into coincidence with the graduation on the y-scale corresponding to the number of degrees in the opposite angle; the remaining sides will be read off opposite the graduations for the remaining angles.

A completely different use can be made of the slide by making both $d(x)$ and $d(y)$ proportional to the squares of x and y. The rule can then be used to read off the hypotenuse of a right-angled triangle whose other two sides are given, or alternatively one side of such a triangle, given the hypotenuse and the remaining side. Special-purpose rules can also be constructed to show the relation between various notes and the keynote in different musical scales, between the exposure time and aperture number for a photographic exposure, and many similar relationships. The usual photographic exposure meter is nothing but a slide-rule, or combination of slide-rules.

It is not necessary to make the rule straight. For some purposes a circular scale is useful; in fact a circular slide-rule has the advantage that it is not necessary to slide the rule through a distance equivalent to a factor of 10, as it often is with the conventional type of rule. Some slide-rules are in fact made with circular scales, one whole circumference corresponding to 10 or 100. Photographic exposure scales are often made in this form. In constructing a home-made rule of this type, polar graph-paper will be found helpful.

6.6. Conclusion

We have only touched the fringe of a very wide subject, but we shall be satisfied if the reader is encouraged to seek for further ideas, and to look out for applications of mathematics in every-day life. The books in the Bibliography which follows will be found useful for further reading. A few of them relate to subjects about which nothing at all has been said in this book. For example, the construction of nomograms for the manipulation of formulae of all kinds is one of the stand-bys of the practical engineer. A nomogram is a versatile tool which can be applied to a wide variety of functional relationships, to the solution of quadratic and cubic equations, the calculation of relative humidity, depth of focus, and many kindred topics. For full details the reader is referred to the book by Brodetsky listed in the bibliography. D'Arcy Thompson's book *On Growth and Form* reveals the remarkable mathematics of the biological world, described in a style that is unique and altogether delight-ful. Current research into the chemistry of the living cell is revealing to us more and more details of the astonishing logical code in which the instructions which govern all living processes appear to be written; written, not in letters of the alphabet nor in mathematical symbols, but in molecules and fragments of molecules arranged in an essentially digital way. The more mechanically minded will find the geometry of pumps, fans, gears, cams, and other mechanisms sufficiently varied to provide considerable mathematical interest.

It has given particular satisfaction to the authors to find that the models described in this book have not only given pleasure to those who have made them, but also have proved a fertile source of new ideas. Serious students of mathematics may find the appropriate model a useful aid to illuminate a difficult concept, but many others have found congenial relaxation in creative activity; and learning proceeds fastest in a pleasurable context. Not a few have found a way of expressing themselves by modify-ing and improving on a model here described, producing in the process something new, beautiful, and satisfying. Of the making of mathematical models there is indeed no end. Let this book serve as a stimulus and a beginning.

BIBLIOGRAPHY

THE following books are suggested for further reading. The authors record with gratitude their indebtedness to many of them, both in stimulating their own interest in models, and in the writing of this book. Several of them are out of print.

A Book of Curves, E. H. Lockwood. Cambridge University Press.

A Companion to School Mathematics, F. C. Boon. Longmans.

A First Course in Nomography, Brodetsky. Bell.

A Rhythmic Approach to Mathematics, Mrs. E. L. Somervell. Geo. Philip & Son (1906).

Analytical Geometry of Three Dimensions, W. H. McCrea. Oliver & Boyd.

Anfertigung mathematischer Modelle, K. Giebel. Teubner, Leipzig (1925).

Chladni Figures, Mary D. Waller. Bell.

Constructing Electric Brains, Berkeley and Jensen. Berkeley Enterprises Inc., Newtonville, Mass.

Craftsmanship in the Teaching of Elementary Mathematics, Westaway. Blackie.

Cubic and Quartic Curves, Basset. Cambridge University Press.

Curves and their Properties, R. C. Yates. Edwards Bros., Ann Arbor.

Curve Tracing, Frost (rev. R. J. T. Bell). Macmillan, and Chelsea (1961).

Encyclopœdia Britannica, XIVth edn., article 'Mathematical Models'.

Experiments in Topology, S. Barr. John Murray.

Geometric Dissections, H. Lindgren. Van Nostrand.

Geometry and the Imagination, Hilbert and Cohn-Vossen. Chelsea (1952).

Harmonic Vibrations and Vibration Figures, ed. H. C. Newton.

How to Draw a Straight Line, A. B. Kempe. Macmillan (1877), and Chelsea.

Introduction to Symbolic Logic, Basson and O'Connor. University Tutorial Press.

Logic Machines and Diagrams, M. Gardner. McGraw-Hill, N.Y.

Mathematical Drawing, Minchin and Dale. Arnold.

Mathematical Games and Pastimes, A. P. Domoryad. Pergamon.

Mathematical Puzzles and Diversions, M. Gardner. Bell.

Mathematical Recreations, M. Kraitchik. George Allen & Unwin.

Mathematical Recreations and Essays, Rouse Ball. Eleventh ed., revised by H. S. M. Coxeter. Macmillan.

Mathematical Snapshots, H. Steinhaus. Oxford University Press, N.Y.

Mathematics and the Imagination, Kasner and Newman. Macmillan.

'Multi-Sensory Aids in the Teaching of Mathematics' (*The 18th Yearbook of the National Council of Teachers of Mathematics*, Bureau of Publications, Teachers' College, Columbia University, N.Y. 1945).

New Mathematical Pastimes, P. A. MacMahon. Cambridge University Press.

On Growth and Form, D'Arcy W. Thompson (abridged edition, ed. J. T. Bonner). Cambridge University Press.

Paper Folding, R. M. Fyfe. Mathematics Teaching Pamphlet no. 8.

Polyominoes, S. W. Golomb. Scribners.

Principles of Mechanism, Dyson. Oxford University Press.

Regular Figures, L. Fejes Tóth. Pergamon.

Regular Polytopes, H. S. M. Coxeter. Methuen.

Soap Bubbles, C. V. Boys. Sheldon Press.

Solid Geometry, L. Lines. Macmillan.

Spinning Tops, J. Perry. Sheldon Press.

Symmetry Aspects of M. C. Escher's Periodic Drawings, Caroline Mac-Gillavry. Oosthoek.

Symmetry Groups, A. Bell and T. J. Fletcher. Mathematics Teaching Pamphlet no. 12.

The Cube made interesting, A. Ehrenfeucht. Pergamon.

The Enjoyment of Mathematics, H. Rademacher and O. Toeplitz. Princeton.

The Graphic Work of M. C. Escher, Oldbourne.

The Language of Mathematics, F. Land. John Murray.

The Third Dimension in Chemistry, A. F. Wells. Oxford University Press.

Tools, A Mathematical Sketch and Model Book, R. C. Yates. Educational Publishers, St. Louis.

Topics in Recreational Mathematics, J. H. Cadwell. Cambridge University Press.

Vielecke und Vielfläche, Max Brückner. Teubner, Leipzig (1900).

Visual Topology, W. Lietzmann. Chatto and Windus.

What is Mathematics?, Courant and Robbins. Oxford University Press.

INDEX

Addition, binary, 263; machine, 265 f., 271.
Adhesives, 16.
Agnesi, M. G., 71.
Algebraic curves, 71.
Alternate segment, 29.
Ampersand, 72.
Amphicheiral knots, 58.
Amplifier, high-gain, 267 f.; torque, 272.
Amsler planimeter, 272.
Analogue computers, 266 f.
Antiprisms, 77, 100, 117.
Anti-snowflake curve, 67.
Apollonius' circle, 32, 73.
Araldite, 16.
Archimedean polyhedra, 60, 77, 80, 100 f., 117, 195; duals, 77, 84, 116; spiral, 73, 241; stellated polyhedra, 123, 135.
Archimedes' theorem, 172.
— trammel, 34, 48, 240.
Area, 20 f., 273; of cone, 170; of sphere, 172.
Astroid, 38, 50, 250.

Balance, Roberval's, 233.
Balsa wood, 17.
Bayko, 15.
Bean curve, 72.
Beats, 74.
Bee's cell, 196.
Bennett, G. T., 239.
Bernoulli, J., 216.
Bernoulli's lemniscate, 42, 73 f., 226, 242.
Bicuspidal curve, 72.
Bifoliate curve, 72.
Binary scale, 259; addition, 263 f.
Bipolar loci, 35, 73.
Blackburne's pendulum, 242.
Borromean rings, 59.
Bostik, 16.
Bottle, Klein, 193.
Bow curve, 72.
Brachistochrone, 216.
Brianchon's theorem, 75.
Bricard chain, 239.
Bridge, N. J., 99.
Bridge, Wheatstone, 266.

Bush differential analyser, 269.
Butterfly curve, 72.

Calculus, propositional, 254.
Cantor set, 67.
Cardboard, 15, 79, 81.
Cardioid, 32, 41, 50, 73.
Cards, punched, 258 f.
Cartesian ovals, 32, 35 f., 73 f.
Cassini's ovals, 32, 73 f., 226.
Catenary, 48, 50 f., 213.
Catenoid, 48.
Cathode-ray oscillograph, 244, 267.
Caustics, 41.
Cement, 16, 80 f., 172.
Centrifuge, 209.
Centrodes, 231.
Chain, 214; Bricard's, 239; spheric, 236.
Chapman, P. B., 207.
Circle, 27 f., 42, 73, 271; coaxal, 75.
Circular functions, 30.
Circular sections, 173.
Cissoid, 32, 42, 71.
Clay, modelling, 198.
Clock, 50.
Close-packing, 196.
Clover-knots, 57.
Cocked hat, 72.
Coin-tossing, 216.
Colouring models, 17, 79, 82.
Compounds, regular, 78, 129.
Computer, analogue, 266 f.; binary, 264 f.; electronic, 260.
Conchoid, 32, 41.
Cone, 169, 182; paradox, 208; sectioned, 167.
Configurations, 75; Desargues's, 161; Reye's, 165.
Conics, 32, 34, 50, 56, 167, 170; confocal, 72.
Connectives, logical, 254, 262.
Cosine, 30.
Courant, R., 215.
Coxeter, H. S. M., 24, 123, 135, 144, 159, 165.
Cross-cap, 191.
Crystals, 84.
Cube, 85, 122, 130, 153; dissected, 202; hexagonal section, 157; snub,